The New Gravitation

KEY TO INCREDIBLE ENERGIES

Other books by H. Arthur Klein

Holography: With an Introduction to the Optics of Diffraction, Interference, and Phase Differences

Fuel Cells: An Introduction to Electrochemistry

Bioluminescence: A first look at light from life

Masers and Lasers

Surfing

Graphic Worlds of Peter Bruegel the Elder

Hypocritical Helena
  — Translated and edited from the works of Wilhelm Busch

Max and Moritz
  — Translated and edited from the works of Wilhelm Busch

By H. Arthur Klein and Mina C. Klein

Temple Beyond Time: The Story of the Site of Solomon's Temple

Peter Bruegel the Elder, Artist of Abundance

Great Structures of the World

Surf's Up! An Anthology of Surfing

The New Gravitation
KEY TO INCREDIBLE ENERGIES

H. Arthur Klein

J. B. Lippincott Company
Philadelphia   New York

The author greatfully acknowledges permission from Random House, Inc.
to use the following excerpts from the poetry of Robinson Jeffers: On page
94, lines from *The Epic Stars*, copyright © 1963; on page 150, lines from
Margrave, copyright 1932; and on page 181, "The Great Explosion" from
The Beginning and the End, copyright © 1963.

To the memory of a mighty thinker whose
contributions to science no longer need
to be demonstrated, and whose commitment
to the cause of man now more than ever
needs to be emulated—
ALBERT EINSTEIN (1879–1955)

Contents

Acknowledgments

For the thirteenth time this author prepares to express thanks to persons whose comments, counsel, or pictorial cooperation have contributed to a book he has written or helped to write. Assuredly the superstition tainting the reputation of thirteen is utterly unscientific; for never before has the author felt luckier regarding the mass and quality of such aid, which it is a privilege as well as pleasant obligation to acknowledge. Where this book manages to shed light into the "black holes" of the new concepts of gravitation, the credit belongs in considerable measure to the following learned, patient, and cooperative persons.

Among authorities based in the West of the U. S. A., special gratitude is offered to Drs. Robert L. Forward (Exploratory Studies Department, Hughes Research Laboratory, Malibu, California) and Donald E. Groom (Department of Physics, University of Utah). Also: Drs. Peter Goldreich, James Gunn, and Maarten Schmidt (all connected with the California Institute of Technology, Pasadena); as well as Drs. L. I. Schiff and William Hamilton (Physics Department, Sanford University).

Among those based in the East, thanks are offered to Drs. Peter G. Bergmann (Department of Physics, Syracuse University, N. Y.), Hong-Yee Chiu (Institute for Space Studies, NASA, N. Y. C.), and Sebastian v. Hoerner (then with the National Radio Astronomy Observatory, Green Bay, West Virginia). Also: Drs. Edwin F. Taylor and Daniel Kleppner (Massachusetts Institute for Technology), Joseph Weber (Physics Department, University of Maryland), John A. Wheeler, and Remo Ruffini (Joseph Henry Laboratories, Princeton University).

Via airmail from overseas arrived invaluable comment in response to queries launched persistently by the author. Thanks are offered to two at Cambridge University: Drs. Dennis W. Sciama (Department of Applied Mathematical and Theoretical Physics) and Martin J. Rees; also to two usually associated with the scientific community of London: Drs. Hermann Bondi (then Director-General, European Space Research), and W. B. Bonnor (Mathematics Department, Queen Elizabeth College, University of London). Likewise, and by no means least, in Scotland: Prof. Norman Feather (Department of Natural Philosophy, The University, Edinburgh).

For permission to use photos or diagrams, or to adapt same for this book, grateful acknowledgment is made to H. W. Harris (Public Information, NASA Lewis Research Center, Cleveland, Ohio); to Dr. J. A. Green, manager, rotational study program, and A. J. Longo, public relations (both of North American Rockwell Space Division, Downey, California). Also and again to Drs. Robert L. Forward (Hughes Research Laboratory and Joseph Weber (University of Maryland).

Thanks are extended also for facilities of many libraries, ranging all the way from the vast book treasury of the British Museum, London; to the Physics Library, UCLA, Los Angeles; and the library of the Hughes Research Laboratory, under Wally Pegram, librarian, and Ed Reese, manager of technical information.

—H. Arthur Klein
Malibu, California, 1971

Foreword

"Incredible grandeur."—That phrase was used by J. Robert Oppenheimer, theoretical physicist, not long before his death in 1967. He was not, however, speaking of nuclear energy, which he helped develop into a dreaded weapon of modern war. He was referring rather to recent observations by astronomers and astrophysicists, revealing enormous and startlingly unaccountable outpourings of energy in the universe, far from Earth.

These observations, together with some earlier ones, have stimulated an exciting upswing in studies of gravitation. This supposedly familiar physical interaction proves to be the only one known which could conceivably provide the titanic floods of power found to come from "quasars," "pulsars," and other objects, whose existence was unknown and even unthinkable till relatively recent days.

This book suggests some ways to *think about* aspects of gravitation that seem most significant for these "incredible grandeurs." It is a first introduction, rather than a full exposition. In fact, it may better be regarded as an "invitation" than an introduction. Its aim is to make somewhat familiar and even attractive some of the novel terms, concepts, and interpretations associated with the "new" gravitation. If it does this, it will realize the fond hope of the author.

The following pages use the convenient shorthand of modern

science. These symbols and abbreviations have a kind of beauty as well as usefulness. We shall have to deal with numbers that are enormous, such as 2,000,000,000,000,000,000,000,000,000,000, which is the mass of our Sun in kilograms. But we shall express it as 2×10^{30} kg, meaning precisely the same thing and vastly easier to work with. We shall deal also with numbers that are almost incredibly tiny, such as 0.0000000000667, which is the numerical part of the important "constant" of universial gravitation, but we shall express that number as 6.67×10^{-11}, identical in meaning, and far handier in every way.

The method of expressing numbers as "powers" of 10 is as simple as it is economical and common in the world of scientific communication. Watch: write 10^2 for 100; 10^3 for 1000; 10^4 for 10,000; 10^5 for 100,000; 10^6 for 1,000,000; and so on, all the way to 10^9 for 1 billion (1,000,000,000); 10^{12} for 1 trillion (1,000,000, 000,000); and so on.

Decimal fractions—numbers less than 1—are dealt with similarly, using a minus sign before the exponent or superscript number. Thus, for 0.1 write 10^{-1}; for 0.01 write 10^{-2}; for 0.001 write 10^{-3}; for 0.0001 write 10^{-4}; and so on.

When we have occasion to multiply two such powers of 10, we simply add their exponents. Thus 1 million times 1 trillion is $10^6 \times 10^{12} = 10^{18}$. And when we divide two such numbers, we subtract their exponents. Thus 1 trillion divided by 10 million is $10^{12}/10^7 = 10^5$, or 100,000.

The incredible grandeurs of gravitation are so very grand, in the sense of large, that every such computational aid becomes a true lifesaver.

Throughout the book, units of the International System (SI) are used. As the approved system for all science, the SI is based on the length unit ot the meter, symbolized by m; the mass unit of the kilogram (kg), where the prefix kilo means 1000; and the time unit of the second (s). The purpose of using one system is to enable scientists all over the world to communicate easily and accurately.

These units relate to our unscientific, obsolescent "everyday" units as follows: 1 foot equals 0.3048 m; 1 yard equals 0.9144 m; 1 inch equals 2.54×10^{-2}m. Furthermore, 1 pound (if we use it as a unit of "mass" rather than "weight") equals 0.453 592 4 kg. The time unit of the second is the same in SI as in everyday usage in the United States. We shall have little need to mention pounds, yards, feet, or inches again in these pages.

Other important SI units will appear, based on the fundamental meter-kilogram-second (MKS) combination. We shall measure force in units of the newton (N), rather than the outdated dyne. (1 newton equals 10^5 dyne). We shall measure energy in units of the joule (J) rather than the erg. (1 joule equals 10^7 erg). We shall measure power, which is the time-rate of energy, in units of the watt (W), remembering that 1 joule per second (1 J/s) is the same as 1 W.

This is the same watt that measures power of all kinds, electrical, mechanical, thermal, and so on. The power consumption of our electric light bulbs is measured in the watt (60 W, 150 W, etc.) and we buy electric current (energy) in an energy unit called the kilowatt hour, meaning 10^3 watts $\times$ 3.6×10^3 s (the number of seconds in 1 hour). The result is that 1 kw-hr equals 3.6×10^6 J, or 3,600,000 joule, in the "longhand" way of writing it.

Still other important variables are measured in this book by means of unit combinations, rather than single units. Thus, velocity is measured in meters per second, symbolized either as m/s or m s^{-1}, which means the same thing. Acceleration—in meters per second per second (m/s^2 or m s^{-2}). Density—in kilograms per cubic meter (kg/m^3 or kg m^{-3}). Pressure—in newtons per square meter (N/m^2 or N m^{-2}), and so on.

In keeping with approved scientific practice, the units, when abbreviated, will be identified always in the singular, rather than the plural. Thus the Sun's mass is 2×10^{30} kg (not kgs), and so on.

At every stage we seek to make clear what physical effects or variables are being measured, and what the numerical results of these measurements or estimates are; and also how the magnitudes of the separate variables change in relation to each other. This is expressed by various compact "recipes" for physical relations, called equations.

In these equations certain italicized symbols will represent constant or unchanging measures. Thus c stands for the velocity of light in empty space, which is very nearly 3×10^8 m s^{-1}. The universal constant of gravitation G has already been mentioned.

Also in these equations we shall use capital letters, unitalicized, to represent physical variables. Thus mass is represented by M, and when two different masses appear in the same equation, such as one for the Earth and the other for the Moon, they are distinguished by subscripts: M_1 and M_2. Lengths may be symbolized by L, or D (for distance), or R (for radius). Time may be symbolized by T, or by P (for a period of duration).

When, in the following pages, the solidus or slash (/) appears, it means simply "is divided by." Thus 1/2 means the same as $\frac{1}{2}$; 1/4 as $\frac{1}{4}$; and, on a larger scale:

$$\text{L}^2\text{M/T means the same as } \frac{\text{L}^2\text{M}}{\text{T}^2} \text{ or } \text{L}^2\text{MT}^{-2}$$

The mathematics used or implied in the following pages goes little beyond arithmetic, and such operations as raising to powers, or the reverse, taking square roots, and so on.

Even readers who shun arithmetic or shy away from equations because they "look strange," should be able to follow most of the ideas we seek to offer. It is possible—or so the author hopes—to take most of this book's mathematics "on faith" although that is by no means the preferred method.

The New Gravitation

KEY TO INCREDIBLE ENERGIES

1

Marvels, Mysteries, Motions

The new era of bold advance in reexamination and extension of gravitational theory really began in the decade of the 1960s, though it drew on important work dating back as far as 1916. That advance is accelerating. It seems certain that—sufficient peace permitting—the 1970s and 1980s will further accelerate this scientific activity and the popular interest in its significance. To stimulate that interest and also to satisfy it to some extent, this book is dedicated.

The "new" insights and suppositions about how gravitation works, or *can* work, under extreme conditions, do amend and amplify the older "classical" views. Those views arose from the seventeenth-century triumphs of Isaac Newton (1642–1727), certainly the outstanding "gravitationalist" prior to that other towering genius Albert Einstein (1879–1955), whose life encompassed scientific achievements and far-reaching humanitarian concerns.

From the latter half of the seventeenth century until early in the twentieth, it was widely assumed that Newton and his disciples had so completely comprehended gravitation that the future could bring no important changes. After all, the rules and recipes deriving from Newton's work sufficed for the calculations used to guide men to the surface of the Moon and back again to Earth. The same body of knowledge should suffice also for "astrogation" of man-made vehicles to, or beyond, Jupiter, giant among the orbiting planets of our Sun.

Newtonian gravitation, however, is no longer sufficient for

dealing with the problems presented by the many amazing observations made with radio and optical telescopes—the same observations whose implications moved Oppenheimer to speak of "incredible grandeur," and which the American Institute of Physics recently described as "the most gigantic, mysterious energy sources in the universe, the radio galaxies and quasars."

This book shall not present the observations that have added to the vocabulary of science such names as quasars, quasi-stellar sources, radio galaxies, Seyffert galaxies, "interlopers," or even the older super-novae, or exploding stars. We shall show why leading theorists have turned to gravitation as the most probable, plausible, and least "incredible" source for the outpourings of power that called forth the phrase "incredible grandeur."

The processes proposed to explain these outpourings of power involve many novel and fascinating concepts. Among them are those bearing names like: neutron star, gravitational collapse, black holes, closed systems, singularities, and Schwarzschild radii. They join with such earlier identified oddities of observation or theory as: dwarf stars, super-dense stars, exploding stars.

Our approach to the "new" gravitational theories will begin via the old, starting with notions near at hand and familiar. Let us look first at how objects around us actually move when they fall or are flung or fired near the surface of Earth, or how they whirl silently through space in the regions beyond our atmosphere. We shall consider here only motions relative to us on Earth—motions that we here can observe and measure.

Some special sorts of motion—Suppose we observe a body B and note, once each second, two measurements: (a) the distance of the body from us, (b) its direction from us. These measurements could be recorded automatically by a radar device. If, second after second, the record reveals no change in either (a) or (b), then we conclude that B is *at rest* relative to us. (Observed from the Moon or Sun, of course, B would be seen to move as the Earth moves.)

Another possibility is this: (b), the direction, remains unchanged, but (a), the distance, grows in proportion to the elapsed time. For example, at the end of 1 s it is 0.5 m more distant than 1 s earlier; at 2 s, 1 m more distant; at 3 s, 1.5 m more distant; at 4 s, 2 m more; and so on.

We find, then, that distance D has a constant, unchanging relationship to elapsed time T. If we symbolize this constant proportion by k, we can summarize it this way: $D/T = k$. In the example given, $k = 0.5$ m s^{-1}. In fact, the constant of proportionality k is here just our old friend, *speed*. And the recipe for speed is D/T, measured always in units of distance divided by units of time, such as miles per hour or meters per second (m s^{-1}).

Science finds *speed* unsatisfactory, for speed does not take into account changes in *direction* of motion. *Velocity*, which includes changes in direction as well as in distance, is a concept used more often in scientific work.

Suppose our radar record showed from second to second no change in the *distance* to body B, but a uniform change in *direction*. The distance to body B might remain unchanged at 10 m, but each second the direction of body B might change by 10 degrees of angle. In 36 seconds it would complete one circuit— a full circle around us.

If we compute the *speed* of body B in its circular path, we find it uniform and unchanging. The *velocity* of body B, however, is something different. It is constantly changing because the body's direction changes in its curved path. Later we shall see that, as a result, the body is constantly *accelerating* toward us at the center, even though its speed, as such, does not gain or lose.

Acceleration at work—When we drive a car along a straight road, as long as the speedometer shows no change, we consider our motion to be uniform. But if the speedometer reading rises, we say that we are "accelerating," and if it falls, we say we are "decelerating," or accelerating negatively.

Suppose that our record shows the following pattern of changes in velocity along a straight path: after 1 s, 2 m s⁻¹; after 2 s, 4 m s⁻¹; after 3 s, 6 m s⁻¹; after 4 s, 8 m s⁻¹; and so on. With each succeeding second the speedometer reads 2 m s⁻¹ more than it did 1 s before.

We would call this a uniform increase in velocity as related to time, or uniform acceleration. There are acceleration patterns that grow or diminish with time; but here acceleration remains steady—a motion pattern especially interesting in the study of gravitation.

Uniform change of *distance* with time means constant velocity (so long as direction does not change). Uniform change of *velocity* with time means constant acceleration.

The first analyst of this very special motion pattern seems to have been a fourteenth-century scholar at Merton College, Oxford, named William Heytesbury. His studies, written under latinized names such as Hentisberus and Tisberius, were really abstract mental exercises, for Heytesbury had not measured such motion patterns anywhere in the real world, and he did not delve into what we know as gravitation.

Heytesbury's great contribution was to show that only when a body's velocity changed uniformly with time, did the total distance moved by that body change in proportion to the *square* of the amount of time that had elapsed.

A useful symbol meaning "is proportional to" is this: $\propto$. We can use it to state Heytesbury's discovery: $L \propto T^2$. It means: "Length moved is proportional to the square of the time elapsed." Or we can more precisely state the same thing by using an equals sign followed by a constant of proportionality, k: $L = kT^2$. By rearranging the equation a little, that becomes $L/T^2 = k$.

What, in this special instance, does k represent? It is simply the *acceleration,* a variable with as much right to its separate existence as velocity, or energy, or power, or force. No matter what the numerical size of an acceleration, it must always be measured in units of length (L) divided by units of time squared

(T^2), such as "miles per hour per second," or "meters per second per second" (m s^{-2}).

If we use A to symbolize acceleration, we get $A = L/T^2$. So long as A remains unchanged, we have uniform acceleration, the very special kind of motion that Heytesbury revealed in Latin to his fellow scholars.

The impasse at Aristotle—More than a century passed after Heytesbury. Scholars did not give much attention to mundane matters such as measurement of how bodies fall or even to celestial matters such as how and why planets move as they do. They thought that all necessary or tenable answers had already been given by that great Greek, Aristotle, or by his interpreters. Those answers included such respected (and false) notions as the following: Heavy bodies drop faster than light ones. They fall as they do because they have, in varying degrees, the innate quality or predisposition called "gravity," which means they cannot rest until they get as near as possible to the depths of the Earth.

There are, however, some other kinds of substance, such as smoke or vapor, which are innately endowed, not with gravity, but with its opposite, "levity." This is the quality that impels them always to rise away from Earth, which they will do unless somehow prevented.

Once the "gravity" or "grave" bodies get down as far as they can go, and once the levity substances have risen as far as possible, they come to rest and remain there. For all objects—so the faithful followers of Aristotle believed and taught—want to arrive, and remain, at rest as soon as they can. They move only when pushed or pulled by some outside force, or by their innate gravity, or levity as the case might be.

Hence, the ever moving planets, the stars, the Sun, and the Moon, all must be kept moving in their courses by some great cosmic machinery. It could be a system of crystalline spheres (one for each planet and a separate one for "the fixed stars" which move as a unit). Perhaps the motions are arranged and supervised by honor guards of attendant angels or spirits especially commissioned for the task.

Some of these ideas are closely akin to the antique mythologies, picturing the Sun carried daily across the heavens in Apollo's flaming chariot.

Leonardo attempts an answer—A real change in attitude and insight is found only when we come, in the latter part of the fifteenth century, to that uncanny forerunner of modern scientific viewpoints, Leonardo da Vinci (1452–1519), a versatile, restless, insatiable genius; a man who was an engineer, inventor, architect, painter, naturalist, anatomist.

In his private notebooks Leonardo set down his attempts to find a pattern in the way bodies fall. He asked himself how much more quickly a body allowed to fall 200 fathoms (1200 feet) would cover the second hundred fathoms than the first. Even to put a question in such quantitative terms was a great step at that time.

Elsewhere in his notebooks Leonardo tried to describe the fall of a heavy body through air of uniform density. His answer is given here in language somewhat modernized, but not distorted. The numbers have been inserted to help us analyze his ideas:

"(1) During each new interval of time it [the body] moves a greater distance than during the preceding interval . . . and likewise reaches a velocity greater than that at the preceding time. (2) Then, in a doubled interval of time, the distance dropped is doubled; and also (3) the velocity of movement is doubled."

Leonardo was right—two out of three times. Statements numbered (1) and (3) are true. However (2) contradicts both (3) and the facts as later observed by Galileo and many others.

To be correct, (2) would have to be changed to " . . . in a doubled interval of time the distance dropped is *quadrupled*."

About a century later, Galileo Galilei (1564–1642) realized, after difficult and patient measurements, that bodies fall or roll

down smooth inclined planes in patterns of uniform acceleration, like that analyzed abstractly by Heytesbury at Oxford. Even
Galileo clung for years to the notion that the velocity of a falling
body increases in proportion to L, the distance the body has
fallen, rather than to T, the time elapsed. Today it is easy to
show that this is an impossible notion, and would result in the
utter inability of objects to start falling. Hindsight so often seems
simple in science, as elsewhere.

Beside unlocking the true pattern of falling motion, Galileo
for all time dispelled the stubborn illusion that heavier objects
fall faster than lighter ones. He probably did not even have to
drop two objects from the top of the Leaning Tower of Pisa to
convince himself that all objects, heavy or light, fall with identical velocities and accelerations (insofar as air resistance does
not distort their motions).

Galileo and others also analyzed another kind of falling and
rising—the swinging of pendulums over short arcs. Here too
the same pattern of acceleration as for the falling stones or balls
fired from siege guns was found: $L/T^2 = A$. In the case of pendulums, L represents lengths, and T the period or time of swings.

But what is the actual amount of the acceleration A that prevails on Earth? It is very nearly 10 m s^{-2}. A closer average figure
is 9.8 m s^{-2}. However, precise measurements of falling objects
and swinging pendulums at various sites show small but significant differences in prevailing accelerations from place to place.

Today the acceleration resulting from gravitation is symbolized
by the small letter g, which can be considered as a reminder
linking the Earth (as in *geo*) with the name of the great Galileo.
There is one official standard acceleration, symbolized by g_o,
and adopted by the International Committee on Weights and
Measures for scientific calculations not directly connected with
specific local situations. That $g_o = 9.80665$ m s^{-2}, which is often
rounded to 9.81 m s^{-2}.

There are also myriads of local accelerations, symbolized by
g_L, for every location on Earth, and even for caves, mines, and

tunnels within the Earth. All the many values of g_L are contained within a rather narrow range of sizes, amounting to about ½ of 1 percent of g_o. These seemingly tiny variations from g_o are of utmost importance to geologists and physicists, for they reveal variations in the Earth's shape and details of the distribution of denser and lighter substances under the ground. (Figure 1-1). In fact, the g_L variations are also related to the effects of the Earth's spin once every 24 hours on its axis. The g_L at a pole, north or south, is about 0.052 m s^{-2} greater than that at the Earth's equator, where "centrifugal force" (outward force on a spinning body) counteracts the pull of Earth to that extent. Sea level observations show a consistent decrease in g_L as one moves along a meridian of longitude from a pole toward the equator.

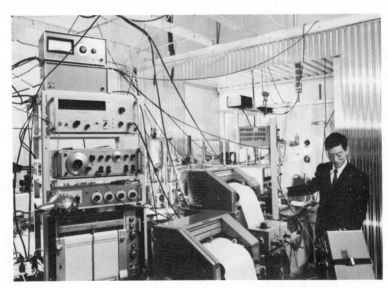

Bureau International des Poids et Mesures, Pavillon de Breteuil, Sèvres, France

Figure 1-1. Finding the Earth's gravitational acceleration with utmost accuracy. Here, at the headquarters of the International Bureau of Weights and Measures, in a lovely park at Sèvres, on the outskirts of Paris, France, Dr. A. Sakuma measures the local acceleration of gravity, g_L, to 8 significant figures. Aided by complex electronic instrumentation, his equipment throws a weight upward and records the precise times when it passes two measured marks on the way up, and again when it passes them as it drops down. A precise equation then converts the four time measures into measures of the gravitational acceleration, measurements that are far more accurate than any obtained before anywhere on Earth.

When the author visited this research headquarters late in 1969, Sakuma's "absolute determination" of g was closest to 9.809 256 6 meters per second per second (m s^{-2}). So ultrasensitive is this technique that a change of a few *centimeters* in the elevation of the equipment will change the final one or two figures. Even the addition of a significant amount of concrete construction in the basement below the apparatus, by adding nearby mass, would alter the final figures.

Although these painstaking measurements apply only to the gravitational acceleration at this particular spot on Earth, they are universally useful. These determinations make it possible to detect any possible "drift" or tendency of that local gravitational acceleration to change, as it would if the universal gravitational "constant," symbolized by G, were changing its magnitude with time.

Dr. Sakuma's equipment is both a kind of "sling shot" for projecting upward the test mass; and also an interferometer, for determining with utmost precision the instants in time when the mirror-system, mounted on that mass, passes the two key points, first on its way up, then again on its way down.

The throwing of the mass takes place in a vacuum. The most accurate measurements are made at night when there is less auto and truck traffic on roads a few kilometers away, and when an automobile factory in the nearby Seine River is stilled.

Beside measuring gravitational acceleration, this super-sensitive device also serves—though not intentionally—as a detector of seismic or Earth motions. The slightest external acceleration, transmitted through its structure, alters the indicated gravitational acceleration. Repeated measurements are essential to average out such external interferences.

But even at uniform distances from a pole, along the same parallel of latitude, the g_L at a high altitude is markedly less than that at sea level. This book, written almost at the 34th degree of latitude and only a few feet above the average level of the nearby Pacific Ocean is the product of a prevailing g_L of about 9.7965 m s^{-2}. Its editor, in Manhattan near the 41st parallel, has a g_L of about 9.80267 m s^{-2}, while the home office of the publisher, in

Philadelphia, Pennsylvania, registers about 9.80196 m s⁻². Readers in Las Vegas, Nevada, at altitude of about 1960 meters, have a relatively low g_L —about 9.79204 m s⁻². And so it goes, with small but very significant local variations of gravitational acceleration.

If the Earth were a perfect sphere, sea level g_L on its equator would be about 0.034 m s⁻² less than it would be at the north and south poles. The actual difference is about 0.014 m s⁻² greater than that, because the Earth is actually oblate, or even slightly pear-shaped, bringing the polar sea level a little closer to the center of the earth than the equatorial sea level.

Beside these gravitational accelerations of Earth there are comparable or contrasting accelerations in space.

Kepler keeps book for the solar system—Johannes Kepler (1571–1630), a persistent German astronomer and mathematician, formulated three laws that describe the orbits he had calculated for the planets then known to circle the Sun.

After careful study of observations, Kepler concluded that the orbits of these planets must be slightly elliptical, rather than perfect circles, and that the Sun must occupy one focus of each such orbital ellipse. (Figure 1-2). The axis passing through this focus and the other empty focus is the major, or longer, axis of the ellipse. Kepler took half of this length as the significant distance of each planet from the Sun.

Then he compared this length L with the period or time T in which each planet completed one full orbit around the Sun. For the Earth, that T is, of course, one "sidereal year," almost exactly 365¼ days. Long, and fruitlessly at first, Kepler studied the figures, seeking some unifying pattern. Finally he hit on a strange but undeniable relationship.

If he cubed the distance ($L \times L \times L = L^3$) and squared the time ($T \times T = T^2$), then L^3 divided by T^2 was a ratio that was almost the same for each planet. In fact, for the entire known family of the Sun, L^3/T^2 equals a constant. Since we measure length by the meter and time by the second, our units for that constant would have to be m³ s⁻², just as our units for acceleration have to be m s⁻², because acceleration is a distance divided by a time squared.

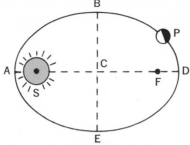

Figure 1-2. The patterns of the planetary paths, Kepler discovered, were ellipses. Here, greatly exaggerated, we see such an orbital ellipse. Its center, at C, lies where its longer axis AD crosses the shorter axis BE. But the central, or sun-like body, marked S is not at the center. It is at one of the two focuses, the generating points for the ellipse. The other, or "empty focus," lies at F. Note that the distance from C to S equals that from C to F. P represents a planet orbiting the sun centered at S.

The eccentricity of an ellipse is measured by dividing the length of the distant CF (center to focus) by the distance CD (center to perihelion, or greatest distance from the center). In this figure, the eccentricity is about 0.68. However, the Earth's orbit shows little eccentricity—only 0.017, and none of the other planets have eccentricities greater than 0.25. Comets and asteroids, however, follow more eccentric, or extended, ellipses.

Kepler not only discovered the elliptical, or eccentric, nature of the planets' orbits, and the fact that the Sun occupies one of the two focal points in each orbital ellipse; he also found the strange uniformity between the time, T, required for one trip around the orbit—as from A, past B, D, E, and back to A; and the average distance L which he took as AD/2, equal to AC or CD in the diagram.

He found that the cube of L divided by the square of T gave a ratio which was the same, or very nearly so, for each of the known planets. As an equation we can say that $L^3/T^2 =$ a constant, or "something significant"—significant, to be sure, of influence emanating from the Sun, around which the planets all move in their unending orbits.

Kepler made also other discoveries about the planetary orbits which we cannot cover here.

Kepler knew of five planets beside the Earth. We know of three more—Uranus, Neptune, and Pluto. For them, too, L^3/T^2 equals the same constant that Kepler pointed out. What do these nine planets, and the countless known asteroids, have in common? All orbit the same central body, our Sun. Something connected with that Sun, or emanating from it, must dictate the single pattern to which all the planets conform. That something we now call *gravitation.*

The relationship $L^3/T^2 = P$ is at the heart of Kepler's Third Law of Planetary Motions. We shall omit his first two laws for the sake of proceeding sooner to the great synthesis of local (earthbound) and celestial (solar-planetary) motions made by Issac Newton, the "Founding Father" of gravitation, a synthesis which serves as a complete and self-consistent scientific tool.

2
The Great Leap — Falling Apple to Orbiting Moon

A standard, but much overworked, anecdote of science history pictures Newton, a young man in his early twenties, at his mother's Lincolnshire farm, spending a vacation from Cambridge University, a vacation enforced by the plague that was then raging. Dozing under an apple tree—so some highly fictional variations suggest—Isaac was struck, presumably on the head, by a falling apple. Thus rudely awakened, he first saw figurative stars, then— if one wants to believe the tales—the real Moon in the sky, and finally he became aware that he had discovered something called "gravitation" as cause both of the nearby apple's fall and the Moon's distant motion.

The facts are, of course, both less abrupt and more impressive. A long, difficult, and sometimes wearisome line of study and trial and error led to Newton's enormous triumphs. By his own later account, Newton had, by the age of twenty-three, begun to think deeply and doggedly about the motions of falling objects and orbiting satellites, such as the Moon and the Sun's planets. But a score of years or more were required before he could overcome obstacles presented by the difficulties of the material and the faulty measurements that were at his disposal.

In comparing the local motions, such as that of the apple, with the distant orbits, such as that of the Moon, Newton naturally had to deal with the two basic variables of length L and time T and with their combinations describing velocity L/T and acceleration L/T^2 Both apple and Moon were moving relative to the Earth.

The earthward acceleration of a Lincolnshire apple had already been measured—the value being just about 9.8 m s^{-2}, as we have seen. But where was to be found an acceleration for the Earth-orbiting Moon? This question was answered at about the same time by a great Dutch scientist, Christian Huygens (1629–1695), and by Newton himself. Huygens and Newton showed that any body B revolving around a center C is actually accelerating constantly toward that center, even though the rate of rotation remains constant. (Figure 2-1). It is a case of a uniform

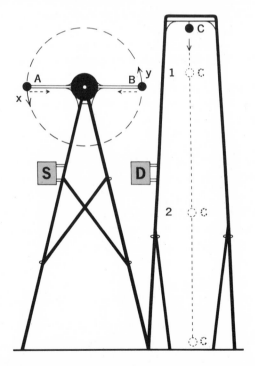

Figure 2-1. Two kinds of acceleration, side by side. At left, labelled S, stands the tower to show acceleration through spinning or rotation. At

right, labeled D, stands the tower to show acceleration by a straight-line drop under the action of gravitation.

If the weight, labelled C, is released from the top, it will fall in 1 second about 4.95 m, to point shown dotted beside the number (1). In 2 seconds it will fall 4 times as far, to about 19.8 m below its release point, shown by dotted outline at (2). And before end of 3 seconds it will hit the ground below the tower. It has been accelerating at a rate of 9.81 m s^{-2}, the standard g, or gravitational acceleration for Earth.

The rotational tower at left has weights A and B each 6.25 m from the center of the shaft on which they are mounted. They are turned at a rate of 1 revolution each 5 seconds. Double arrows show direction of revolution. Dotted arrows show direction of their acceleration—toward the center of rotation.

The equation for rotational acceleration developed by Huygens and Newton shows that each weight, A and B, will be accelerated toward that center at just about the same rate as the standard g —namely, 9.81 m s^{-2}. If the rate of their revolution were doubled, that acceleration would increase four times. If the length of the arms that hold them out from the center were doubled, their acceleration centerward would also be doubled.

Every orbiting planet or moon accelerates *toward* the body around which it orbits. Acceleration takes place both rotationally and in dropping or "speeding up" in a straight line.

circular *speed* being nevertheless an acceleration because of the curvature of the path. Variable speed in a straight line produces acceleration; and so does uniform speed over a curved course. Huygens and Newton supplied a simple equation for the amount of acceleration A of an object revolving at a radius of rotation of length L in a period of time of T per rotation:

$$A = \frac{4\pi^2 L}{T^2}$$

The π is the familiar ratio between a circle's circumference and its diameter: 3.14159. Hence the constant $4\pi^2$ equals very nearly 39.5. This "recipe" for the acceleration resulting from every rotation is used constantly in science. Figure 2-2 shows an elaborate and expensive "rotational facility," the largest in

Figure 2-2. World's largest whirl-around, constructed to create acceleration effects through uniform rotation. At North American Rockwell's plant, Downey, California, this half-million-dollar device was built for the National Aeronautics and Space Administration, to study how men would be affected by long residence in revolving space stations. The car, 40 feet long, can contain 4 men, at a distance (D) of 75 feet from the rotational hub, seen here at the center.

When the period of rotation, T, is 15 seconds (or 4 rpm), as shown by the Huygens-Newton equation, occupants of the car experience an acceleration of about 4 meters per second per second, or about 40 percent of the gravitational acceleration on Earth (g_o). When the rotation is increased to a T of 10 s (or 6 rpm) then the occupants in the car experience rotational acceleration more than 90 percent that of normal on Earth (g_o).

Tentative plans for future space stations suggest they may look like giant dumbells, constantly revolving in space at about 4 rpm. Their astronaut occupants may work at a radius (D) of about 90 feet and so experience about 50 percent of normal g_o, but they would sleep at a radius of about 60 feet from the center of rotation, where they would experience only some 30 percent of the g_o prevalent (as an average) on Earth. (They would always be aware, however, of the so-called "Coriolis effect," which we on Earth do not notice because of our large D.)

By such rotation-engendered acceleration it is hoped to avoid the dangerous physical effects to be feared from prolonged space-living in a condition of complete "weightlessness." Such giant spinning "dumbell" stations may be orbiting at velocities or 17 or 18 thousand mph, while they are kept spinning at the preselected rate of about 4 rpm, equal to a period T of 15 s. Precise control of the rotational rate is, of course, essential to the plan.

the world, which studies how men in future rotating "space stations" would be affected by revolving environments. The extent of such man-made acceleration is predicted by the Huygens-Newton recipe, based on the rotational radius and the period per rotation of the facility.

Newton was very familiar with the Moon's orbital period, which is just about 2.36×10^6s, an astronomical month. But what was the magnitude of L, the radius at which the Moon orbits the Earth and accelerates toward it? The observations available to Newton showed that the Earth-to-Moon distance L must be slightly more than 60 times the Earth's own radius R. To be quite exact, L here is the distance between the centers of Earth and Moon, not between their external surfaces.

When Newton began serious work on this great problem, the best available estimates of the actual size of the Earth put the Earth's radius R at about 5.72×10^6m. We now know that that was about 15 percent less than the correct measurement.

Newton had to work with the most reliable figures then available. His first calculations showed that the apple's earthward acceleration (9.8 m s^{-2}) was about 4150 times the earthward acceleration of the Moon. But the hypothesis Newton was testing called for the apple to accelerate earthward about 3600 times as much as the Moon, for the Moon was 60 times as far from Earth's center as was the apple, and 60^2, or 60×60, is 3600.

The discrepancy between 3600 and 4150 times was too great for Newton to feel that his hypothesis was supported. This hypothesis—that gravitation diminished as the inverse square of the distance over which it acted—had to be set aside for the time being, though Newton did not forget it.

Science moves ahead largely on roads whose foundations are formed by ever more accurate measurements. Shortly before 1670 a careful French surveyor, Jean Picard, led an expedition to measure the length of the "arc of the meridian." The results, vastly more accurate than any before, showed the Earth about

15 percent larger in linear dimensions than had previously been believed.

Newton now returned again to his problem. In the phrase popular among twentieth-century scientists, he took the new figures and "plugged them into" his previous equations. These figures showed the Moon's earthward acceleration to be substantially less than it had appeared before. In present day units, the Moon was found to be constantly "falling" earthward with an acceleration of some 0.0027 m s^{-2}. This, times 3600, came unmistakably close to the 9.8 m s^{-2} acceleration of bodies falling at Earth's surface.

In his quaint seventeenth-century wording, Newton told later how, after comparing the two diverse accelerations in the light of the squares of the distances at which they were observed, "I found them answer pretty nearly."

Only after this confirmation was Newton willing to proceed, develop in full his theories of gravitation and motion, and finally publish his masterpiece in Latin, the *Principia,* generally regarded as the most influential single work of science in history. The *Principia* included, among many things, the difficult geometrical proof that a spherical body such as Earth, Moon, or Sun gravitates *as if* its entire mass were concentrated at its center. Hence the constant emphasis on lengths L measured between the centers of bodies, not between their surfaces.

It is interesting that Newton did not actually work with accelerations as such, but with a kind of equivalent. He used the total distances that the bodies—apple or Moon— would fall earthward in the lengthy period of 60 s (1 minute). For the Moon, he found that distance to be about 3.64 m, in modern units. But in the case of the falling object near the Earth—the "apple"— this distance was enormous: about 17,770 m.

Actually, Newton took some liberty here. The fact is that a body allowed to drop from 17,770 m above the surface of Earth would fall for a period somewhat *longer* than 60 s, because at the start of its fall (17,770 m up) it would obey an acceleration about 0.057 m s⁻² less than that at the lower level, down in the Lincolnshire orchard. In fact, as it fell that great distance, the g to which it responded would increase by more than one-half of 1 percent.

Newton, of course, was not misled. He merely had oversimplified for convenience in making a point—as we also seek to do many times in this book.

Newton established the great principle that for any central body, such as the Sun or Earth, the accelerations of objects falling toward it or orbiting around it will be in inverse proportion to the square of the distances that separate the centers of those objects from the center of the major body to which they respond.

Since an apple falls earthward at the surface with a g of 9.8 m s⁻², what would be the characteristics of a satellite orbiting the Earth just barely clear of its surface? Newton's equations show that the satellite would have to circle the globe once every 84.4 minutes, at a speed of about 79,000 m s⁻¹, which is about 23 times the velocity of sound.

Any such satellite would, of course, burn up instantly, as meteors do when they plunge into the denser atmosphere near the surface of Earth. Nevertheless, the concept of the period for such a surface orbit is an important one (Figure 2-3).

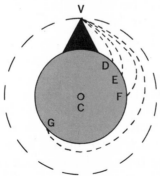

Figure 2-3. From trajectories to orbits. This is a famous figure, from the "founding father" of scientific gravitation, Isaac Newton. Based on a

diagram in Newton's *De Systemate Mundi,* this shows the Earth with its center at C. From the summit of a tall mountain, V, bodies are projected with different velocities. The slowest moving body falls to the ground closest to the foot of the mountain, at D. A swifter moving one reaches E; a still swifter one reaches F; and the swiftest of the "falling" bodies gets as far as G.

However, Newton noted that "if the velocity was still more augmented, it would reach at last quite beyond the circumference of the Earth, and return to the mountain from which it was projected." The artillerist (if a gun did the projecting) would thus be in danger of being struck in the back of his head!

Thus Newton linked the trajectories of bodies that fall to the ground with the trajectories of those that circle or orbit, always "falling," but never reaching the ground, for the ground "falls away" below them at a like rate.

The artificial satellites that men have placed in orbit around Earth have moved at levels of 300 km or more above Earth's surface, in order to escape the atmospheric drag, which remains serious even as high as 50 to 100 km.

Including Kepler— In his triumphant *Principia,* Newton dealt with accelerations, momentums, forces, actions and reactions, and inertias. He showed that his basic equations included the constant L^3/T^2 ratio that Kepler had noted for the Sun's planets.

Newton also showed that his equations included the two relations forming Kepler's First and Second Laws of planetary motion: the orbits are ellipses, with the Sun always at one focus, and the planets move in these orbits at speeds inversely proportional to their distances from the Sun.

Newton provided the mathematical "recipes" or equations relating the orbits of the planets to their varying distances from the Sun and to the mass of the Sun itself. He did the same for the orbit of the Moon with respect to its parent body, the Earth. Newton's basic "recipes," in more sophisticated form, are still used to plan and correct the orbits of man's artificial satellites.

Today's tools for space navigation, or "astrogation," are equations rather than geometrical constructions. There are equations for computing the orbital velocity of a satellite at all times within a circular orbit, or in all possible elliptical orbits.

For simplicity we deal here with circular orbits, where the radius remains unchanged, as does the velocity in orbit, and the acceleration earthward because of the rotary motion.

Rockets are used to "inject" the satellites they carry into a more or less predetermined orbit around Earth. There are various possibilities for directions of travel at the moment when the man-made satellite disengages from the rocket that has boosted it into orbit. If the satellite, moving at right angles to the direction toward Earth, is travelling at just the velocity of a circular orbit at that distance, it will follow that full circle. However, if at the moment of "injection" into orbit the satellite's velocity is somewhat greater, it will follow an elliptical orbit. The point of its injection then will be the "perihelion," or closest approach to the central body (Earth); while the satellite will reach its greatest distance from Earth 180 degrees away, at the opposite end of the ellipse.

Suppose at the moment of injection velocity is somewhat less than that for a full circular orbit. Then that point will be the one of greatest distance from Earth, and will reach its perihelion 180 degrees away at the opposite side of the orbit. In fact, if velocity at injection is too low, the satellite's "fall" closer to Earth will bring it into dense atmosphere and will perhaps cause it to crash on Earth.

There is another and very different danger. If velocity at injection is more than 1.414 (square root of 2) times the circular orbital velocity at that radius, then the satellite will break its orbit and move off on one branch of a hyperbola or parabola, curves which will not bring it back again toward Earth. It will have attained "escape velocity," which is always just 1.414 times the circular velocity at any given radius around a central body.

Weight versus mass — Consider the moment of lift-off of a great rocket designed to launch astronauts into orbit. At the count of zero, the enormous engines are ignited, vast masses of hot gas rush earthward with combined thrust measured in possibly millions of pounds, or the metric force unit, the newton.

The equal-and-oppositeness of action and reaction, stressed by Newton in his *Principia,* shows itself as the great rocket first hangs free an instant, then accelerates upward, its velocity constantly growing.

The astronauts in their protective seats or couches experience sensations of increased weight. Before lift-off their bodies sought to move in response to a g_L of about 9.8 m s^{-2}. Now, if their rocket vehicle attains an acceleration away from Earth of 9.8 m s^{-2}, they experience a "force" of 2 g_L. A man whose weight was measured at 50 kg before, now feels as if he weighed 100 kg. The mass of matter in his body has not changed, but the force he exerts on his supports has altered drastically.

We all encounter periods when accelerations seem either to increase or decrease our customary weights. The increasing speed of an airplane along a runway, or of a drag racer on the strip, presses us back with added "weight" against the seat. The dropping of an elevator makes us feel strangely, perhaps disturbingly, lighter.

Newton used the word *force* to name the processes which accelerate objects. If the object remains unchanged, the force associated with it should have a constant relation to the resulting acceleration. That relation depends on the amount of matter, or *mass,* in the object.

What we call "weight" is a force, resulting from the refusal of supports to allow us, or other objects, to fall freely in response to g_L. The same mass that exerts a downward push of 1 kg-force on Earth, will push downward with barely one-sixth that force on the Moon, where the g is correspondingly lower.

But en route from Earth to Moon, in a space vehicle that is coasting, without the push of its jets, that same mass will exert *no force* downward, or in any other direction, on other objects moving as it does. It will have become "weightless," though its mass has not altered.

Our concern here is to note that the state of "weightlessness" does not result from nullification of gravitational effects. It results from complete and unchecked *response* to those effects. Such response may take the form of continuous orbits or of coasting in open trajectories, which includes falling unchecked toward an attracting body, such as the Earth or Sun.

The most effective device for eliminating awareness of *g* or "weight" without leaving the Earth is the great ZGRC (zero gravity research facility), extending from the Earth's surface 500 feet down at the Lewis Research Center of the National Aeronautics and Space Administration, Cleveland, Ohio (Figures 2-4 and 2-5).

NASA Lewis Research Center

Figure 2-4. On the way to weightlessness. An experiment weighing three-quarters of a ton is here readied for a drop down the 500-ft concrete tube of the Zero Gravity Research Facility of NASA's Lewis Research Center, Cleveland, O.

A drop from top of shaft to botton results in 5 seconds of "weightlessness" or zero-*g* for the contents of the carrier. The concrete lined shaft is 28 feet in diameter and contains a steel vacuum chamber 20 feet in diameter, which can create low pressures similar to those found at altitudes of 50 miles above the Earth.

NASA Lewis Research Center

Figure 2-5. Free fall will mean freedom from the force effects that we call "weight." Looking up past the steel vacuum chamber at the suspended test-object-carrier of the monster Zero Gravity Research Facility.

Though this test involves dropping three-quarters of a ton of total weight, the installation can drop as much as 6 tons, to secure a significant 5 seconds of weight-free state. By yielding to gravitational acceleration, the tested objects appear to lose all "weight."

Test "carts" can be dropped down the shaft to provide up to 5 seconds of zero-*g* for their contents. At the bottom of the drop the carts are quickly brought to a stop, without damage to their contents. The deceleration is as great as if an automobile travelling at 120 miles an hour were halted within 15 feet.

If still longer periods of zero-*g* are needed, the cart is shot upward from the bottom of the shaft, rising during 5 seconds, then dropping back again during another 5—travelling for a total of ten seconds. Air pressure in the shaft can be lowered to that of altitudes about 80 km above Earth's surface, to reduce resistance to motion. With this huge zero-*g* device, engineers have been studying how liquid fuels shape themselves when "weightless." These, and many other problems of weightless behavior, keenly concern space designers and technicians.

Other zero-*g* tests are made by flying a large airplane in a carefully calculated trajectory. That trajectory is the portion of an ellipse which, if extended through the solid Earth, would have its distant focus at the very center of the Earth. Such a trajectory, which permits passengers in the plane to tumble and float weightlessly for many seconds, is sometimes called a "parabola." The trajectory is, however, a segment of an ellipse—a piece of an orbit which could exist in full only if the Earth's mass were shrunken to a tiny ball around the center of our great sphere.

In all these weightless tests, the objects tested retain their masses unchanged, but are freed from the usual force effects which we call "weight."

How many kinds of mass?—In science and engineering *mass* is an essential word and idea. We have already noted that the internationally adopted system of scientific units of measurement, known for short as the SI, is based on the three fundamentals of the meter of length, the second of time, and the kilogram of *mass* (not of weight).

"Weight" is simply our name for the force that results when the local acceleration g_L acts on a mass that is not allowed to respond freely (fall) in answer to that acceleration. When an unchanging mass is taken from place to place on Earth, it shows different weights because of the different accelerations. Hence, *weight* is too erratic for the needs of modern science, which uses *mass* as one of its basic units along with the basic units of length and time.

The worldwide standard of mass is the prototype kilogram, a small cylinder of platinum and iridium alloy, painstakingly protected in an underground vault at the headquarters of the International Bureau of Weights and Measures, within a lovely park at Sèvres, near Paris, France.

We see the prototype (Figure 2-6) surrounded by three concentric bell jars, like a metal monarch; and in attendance roundabout, like courtiers, stand six "seconds," or reserve kilogram masses, duplicating with extreme precision the proto- type. Every major nation, in its bureau or institute of standards, has at least one precise duplicate of the Sèvres prototype.

Figure 2-6. Mass everywhere is measured in relation to this well-guarded small cylinder of platinum-iridium. The K symbol around the neck of the second of the three concentric bell-jars surrounding the cylinder indicates that here (center) sits the world's scientific standard of mass—

the kilogram. All others, including the 6 clustered around it, are precise duplicates of the original.

The size of the cylinder is modest, as suggested by the black tube above which contains the platinum-iridium bar one meter (39.37 inches) long that formerly served as the world standard of length. It is now dethroned, its place being taken by light-waves which can give far more accurate and reporducible length comparisons.

One must constantly recall that this international kilogram is a unit of *mass,* not of weight. (Weight is a matter of *force,* measured in newtons.)

Science never calls these "weights." They are unit *masses.* Weight is a force, the product of a mass by an acceleration. The international kilogram of mass is related to force only by the official "recipe" for the newton (N), the sole unit for force recognized in the SI unit system:

The *newton* (unit of force) is that force which gives to a mass of 1 kilogram an acceleration of 1 meter per second per second.

That acceleration and the resulting force must be measured in the same *direction.* Both these variables involve direction as well as magnitude. This is true also of other important variables: velocity, acceleration, and even length. The newton, as the scientific unit of force, is derived from the three basic units in this way: $1 \text{ N} = 1 \text{ Kg m s}^{-2}$. It has the same recipe as a mass times an acceleration. If we represent force by F and acceleration by A, then $F = MA$.

We can rearrange this fraction, so that $M = F/A$. This shifts the emphasis, reminding us that mass can be regarded as the ratio between a force (numerator) and the resulting acceleration (denominator). In terms of units, we can say that the mass in kilograms is obtained by dividing the force in newtons by the produced acceleration, in m s^{-2}.

During the centuries that followed Newton's great synthesis of gravitation and the basic laws of motion, one simple but deeply significant truth was usually overlooked: There are really two, or even three, kinds of "mass."

One is the kind referred to in the definition of the unit of force, the newton, quoted from the publications of the International Bureau of Weights and Measures. That kind is the mass which measures the *inertia,* or the "reluctance" of a body to respond to a force by accelerating. This can be called inertial mass or inertial magnitude, and can be symbolized by M_i.

Next is the kind of mass that related a gravitational acceleration, (g_L) to the resulting downward force or "weight." We could call this gravitational mass or magnitude, and symbolize it by M_g. Or we can be even more analytical and say that every body, from a pin to a planet, has two kinds of gravitational magnitude: (a) the passive, according to which it reacts to gravitational fields; and (b) the active, according to which it creates or generates gravitational fields. We could symbolize those, respectively, by M_p and M_a, for passive and active.

Here is a simple though crude analogy. M_a could be likened to the summons or command issued by a gravitating body in the form of its "field." M_p could be likened to the perception of that summons by the passive or responding body. And M_i could be likened to that body's physical lethargy, or reluctance to get into motion. Fortunately, we need not deal in such psychological terms. We can assume here that M_a is always exactly proportional to M_p. We do so when we say that the force with which the Earth attracts the Moon is precisely equal to the force with which the Moon attracts the Earth. In the first case the mass of Earth is the M_a, that of the Moon the M_p. In second case, the opposite holds true.

We shall thus consider both M_a and M_p to be identical aspects of M_g, the gravitational magnitude or mass of an object. That leaves us still with the great mystery, mostly disregarded during the centuries after Newton: Why should the proportion between the M_g and the M_i for any body be always identical?

The force that accelerates a body in inverse proportion to its M_i may be supplied by muscular, mechanical, or electrical means, as well as by the "pull" or force of gravitation. There is no *logical* reason, or was not before Einstein's relativity theories, why balls of two quite different substances, iron and gold for instance, should respond with exactly the same acceleration when dropped from a height.

Suppose the balls are identical in mass, although that is not really necessary for this analysis. The mass in which they are identical is the inertial mass M_i. That can be tested readily if we apply to each of the balls the identical force by means of springs and find that they acquire the same acceleration when sliding on a smooth level sheet, where no *gravitational* changes are involved.

This still does not give us grounds to assume that the M_g or gravitational magnitudes of the balls are identical. For example, if we found that the iron ball fell somewhat faster than the gold, we should have to conclude that iron's ratio of M_i/M_g is less than the same ratio for gold. In other words, we would conclude that the gold has less gravitational magnitude (M_g) relative to its inertial magnitude (M_i) than does the iron.

Such findings would be most significant. They have been calculated again and again. Not the slightest variation has been found among all the many substances tested. The latest tests, conducted under R. H. Dicke at Princeton, were delicate enough to have detected differences of 1 part in a million times a million (10^{12}). Our conclusion is that an invariable ratio exists between M_i (the inertial reluctance to be accelerated) and M_g (the gravitational response or potency) of a body.

"This conclusion," Einstein declared, "could not have been foreseen, and is based on observation, not reason." He went on to ask whether the direct relation between the two kinds of mass was merely an accident, or whether it held clues to deeper physical meanings.

Science prior to Einstein had treated the complete correspondence between M_i and M_g as if it were a mere accident. Einstein however, had the insight to see this correspondence as something fundamental. He made of it a stepping stone leading to the relativistic geometries of space-time, in which space and time are inextricably merged, according to equations of great beauty and elegance.

The presence of each and every mass produces a "warp" or "cavity" in this space-time. Only in matterless space is it a uniform "flat" sheet—to use an oversimplified picture. The greater the amount of mass, the deeper the cavity or warp in space-time. And if the mass is compacted to great density, so that the gravitational potential at its surface is especially high, then in that region of space-time the warp is steepest and deepest.

What we call orbits and trajectories are, in the space-time geometry of relativity, merely the inevitable "shortest distances between two points" on the curved space-time "surface." Each and every body, no matter what its mass, must pursue the same path when moving through the same part of the field around a gravitating body. Thus relativity does not need the cumbersome apparatus of "forces" that is unavoidable in Newtonian gravitation analysis. And thus relativity resolves or utilizes the striking and unalterable identity between the two kinds of mass, the inertial (M_i) and the gravitational (M_g).

In the classical or Newtonian approach, only one kind of mass is recognized, symbolized here merely by M. It serves both for the gravitational and the inertial situations. The two best known equations associated with the work of Newton make use of this "catchall" kind of mass:

$F=AM$, meaning that a force is measured by that acceleration it produces in a known mass; or that a mass is defined by a known force divided by the resulting acceleration of the body whose mass is in question.   (1A)

The other equation also defines force—the gravitational attractive force that any two bodies in the universe, M_1 and M_2, exert, each on the other. This mutual force, or rather these two equal and opposite forces (on M_1 toward M_2, and on M_2 toward

M₁), Newton defined in relation to the distance D separating their respective centers of mass:

$$F_{grav} = \frac{p M_1 M_2}{D^2} \tag{1B}$$

Here p is a constant of proportionality, part of a relationship that remains the same, no matter what changes occur from case to case in the values for M_1, M_2, and D. But p is not the symbol by which this constant is everywhere represented and used. Sometimes the constant is represented by k, but here and most often elsewhere, it is represented by capital G. This is, in fact, Newton's gravitational constant, and must never be confused with g (little g), symbol for accelerations resulting from gravitation.

Sometimes a minus sign is used following the equals symbol in equation (2) to indicate gravitational force. It is a matter of convention and convenience whether or not such forces are treated as "deductions" or "assets." Here we use no minus sign.

One small observation will show why a minus sign *could* be used in this case. When we deal with the forces between electric charges, we find that the charges attract each other only when one charge is negative, the other positive: in other words when they are *unlike* charges. *Like* charges, on the contrary, repel each other.

The product of a minus charge and a plus charge is a minus quantity, associated in the electrical case with attractive forces. Whereas, like charges, whether both are negative or both positive, always have a positive product, which is associated with repulsive forces. Hence in the electrical case, which otherwise has many close analogies to the gravitational case, we can consider attractive forces as negative and repulsive forces as positive.

Now, gravitating masses are all alike. There is no plus or minus. And they always interact by attracting each other. We could, accordingly, call gravitational force (F_{grav}) a negative magnitude. But it seems clearer and simpler not to.

We shall reserve the use of the minus sign for two other measures of gravitation soon to be introduced: gravitational potential (ϕ) and gravitational, or binding, energy.

The "Big G" has manifold uses. It is a kind of general key to gravitational effects. It links them, or proportions them, to the variable physical measures involved: to the masses, big or little, and to the inter-mass distances.

We shall see some of the secrets that can be unlocked with the help of the Big G, whose actual numerical value turns out to be extraordinarily tiny.

3

Newton's Big G, and Four Tools Fitted to Measure Gravitation

We now have at hand two universal equations for force. Equation (1A), $F = MA$, applies to any case where a body of mass M acquires acceleration A from the action of a force F, whether that force be exerted by living muscles, a steam engine, a diesel tractor, electric charges, magnets, or gravitational "attraction." Equation (1B) is confined to forces resulting from gravitational "attraction." As a reminder we give it the subscript meaning "gravity":

$$F_{grav} = \frac{GM_1M_2}{D^2} \tag{2}$$

If both these equations are valid, then any allowable combination of the two must be valid also. Let us combine them and see.

Consider a Lincolnshire apple whose mass is M_2. It is attracted by the entire Earth, whose mass M_1 behaves as if it were all concentrated at the very center of the globe, just one Earth radius (D) distant from the apple.

The first equation tells us that the downward force (weight) exerted by the apple must be $F = M_2A$, or the mass of the apple times an acceleration—which is obviously the gravitational acceleration g_L prevailing in that particular orchard.

That same downward force (weight) exerted by the apple hanging on the tree is also measured by the other equation as the constant G times the masses of the apple (M_2) and the Earth (M_1), divided by the square of the distance (D^2) between their centers. Combining equations (1) and (2) we find:

$$\underset{\text{(1)}}{} \qquad \underset{\text{(2)}}{}$$

$$\text{Weight of apple} = F_{grav} = M_2 A = \frac{GM_1M_2}{D^2}$$

$$\text{Hence it is clear that } M_2 A = \frac{GM_1M_2}{D^2}$$

And since M_2 is a factor on both sides of this equality, it can be cancelled, leaving us with

$$A = \frac{GM_1}{D^2} \tag{3}$$

In words, the local acceleration g_L anywhere on Earth should equal G times the Earth's total mass, divided by the square of the distance to the mass-center of Earth. Obviously that acceleration g_L is independent of the mass of the particular objects accelerated downward. Apples, andirons, automobiles, or aviators—all fall with the same acceleration, as Galileo knew and experience confirms.

Now we have two equations, each of which includes G, the gravitational constant whose actual size we have not yet revealed.

We can rearrange equation (2) so that it takes this form:

$$G = \frac{F_{grav}\, D^2}{M_1 M_2} \tag{4}$$

And we can rearrange equation (3) so that it becomes:

$$G = \frac{AD^2}{M_1} \tag{5}$$

Since A is here the local acceleration of gravity, equation (5) can also be written this way:

$$G = \frac{g_L D^2}{M_1} \qquad (6)$$

Now, if we can measure the variables to the right of the equals signs in either (4) or (6) above, we should be able to supply the numerical value for G at the left. First, however, let us see in what units G must be measured. From (6) we can see the units can include those which measure acceleration (m s^{-2}), times those that measure a distance squared (m^2), divided by the unit that measures mass (kg). That unit combination must be m s$^{-2} \times$ m^2/kg, which is most compactly written as m^3 kg^{-1} s^{-2}, or in words "meters cubed per kilogram per second squared." That is, then, one unit combination in which G can be measured.

From equation (4) we can get another combination of units. They will look different, but mean the very same thing. Here we see that G can be measured by a force (in units of the newton), times a distance squared (m^2), divided by the product of two masses (kg^2). The unit combination is thus N m^2/kg^2, more compactly written as N m^2 kg^{-2}, and in words described as "newtons times meters squared per kilogram squared."

To repeat, the meaning of m^3 kg^{-1} s^{-2} is identical with that of N m^2 kg^{-2}. They are just two different ways to express, in units, the same relationship; just as N means the same as m kg s^{-2}, and acceleration A means the same as m s^{-2}.

How big is Big G?   Newton himself made a rather good guess as to what the numerical value of G would be when it could some day be measured. Those first measurements, however, were not made until a century or more after Newton had introduced his G to the world. Even today the work of measuring it more accurately is far from ended. Nevertheless, Newton's analysis of gravitation triumphed. His analysis did not require a separate value for G, since it used the product $G \times M$ for the important cases where M meant the mass of the Earth, or the Sun, or the Moon, or of any of the planets. G, in short, remained always part of a gravitational "package."

Long, tedious, painstaking experiments were required to find a separate or "absolute" value for G. Such tests have often been called, rather picturesquely, "weighing the Earth," since they made it possible for the M of the Earth to be extracted from the product $G \times M$.

The present best numerical value for G is 6.674×10^{-11} N m^2 kg^{-2} or m^3 kg^{-1} s^{-2}. Those two alternative unit combinations, we have seen, mean the same thing physically. It is a matter of convenience which unit combination we use. The numerical part (6.674×10^{-11}) is the same either way.

Since G is one of the great universal constants of science, its numerical value is most important. That value today is known to about 1 part in 1700. In other words, the odds are about 999 to 1 that the true value is not less than 6.670 nor more than 6.678. G has thus been determined with less precision than the other fundamental constants of science. This fact reflects the many difficulties of dealing with forces so feeble as those which can be produced in gravitational experiments under Earth conditions.

Even now, further experiments, with ever more sophisticated and ingenious devices, are going on. They should substantially reduce our uncertainty regarding the numerical value of G. Most tables used by scientists give this value simply as 6.67×10^{-11} followed by either of the appropriate unit combinations.

Here we shall not describe any of the actual equipment used in measurements to determine the value of G. Instead, for brevity, we shall show an imaginary arrangement that is simpler by far than actual possibilities permit. Here (Figure 3-1) we seek to measure G directly by placing two unit masses (1 kg each) with their centers separated by unit distance (1 m). Mass A is anchored. Mass B, however, can move horizontally in response to the gravitational force that attracts it toward A.

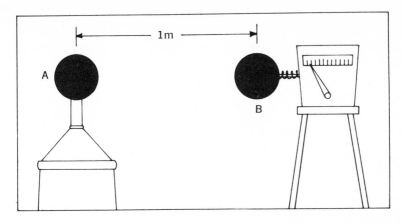

Figure 3-1. Imaginary test setup, symbolizing measurements to determine the actual magnitude of G, the universal constant of gravitational effects. If A and B have each exactly 1 kg mass and their centers are just 1 m apart, then the force with which B (movable) is attracted to A (fixed) will be *numerically* equal to G. G is not itself an amount or magnitude of force, as the text makes clear.)

A "force meter" is connected with B to measure, in newtons, the strength of B's response toward A. Since we use unit masses and unit distance, this meter should show a force of just 6.67×10^{-11} N. This is a fantastically tiny force, for 1 N is equivalent to the downward force (weight) of just 0.1 kg (100 grams); or of about 0.224 pounds. Working with unit masses at unit distance, we produce a force which is less than one ten-billionth of the weight of 100-grams mass on Earth. Even if we increase our test masses manyfold and place them as close as possible without touching, the resulting gravitational forces remain seemingly infinitesimal.

The devices actually employed to measure G operate in high vacuum, and often at low temperatures, so that the motions of residual atoms shall not introduce forces that will obscure those of gravitational attraction. This is one more aspect of the great apparent paradox: gravitation is, by all odds, the feeblest force or interaction known to us; yet it is also the only interaction capable, in extreme conditions, of the most stupendous and cataclysmic outpourings of power that the universe does, or seemingly can display.

G, a force-shaper, not a force—Often one finds statements that G is a "force." It is not. If it were a force, it could be measured in the newton, unit of force, and nothing more. As we have seen, it must be measured in newtons times meters squared divided by kilograms squared (N m^2 kg^{-2}). Only if we arbitrarily use 1 m as our distance and use masses of 1 kg each for our attracting bodies, do we get a force that is equal (numerically equal) to G.

G is really, and should be thought of as, a constant of proportionality. It sets the ratios, or proportions, between (a) the gravitational effects, such as forces or accelerations; and (b) the physical situations, such as the masses and the distances, which give rise to those effects. G is not a force; it is really a "force shaper," or an "acceleration shaper," or even a "gravitational energy shaper."

With the numerical value for G at hand, let us test it on equation (3): $g = GM/D^2$. We know that the Earth's mass M is about 6×10^{24} kg; also that the radius of Earth D is about 6.4×10^6 m; finally, that G is 6.67×10^{-11} m^3 kg^{-1} s^{-2}. If we put this all together it becomes:

$$g = \frac{(6.67 \times 10^{-11}) \times (6 \times 10^{24})}{(6.4 \times 10^6)^2}$$

This works out to the following fraction:

$$\frac{40.02 \times 10^{13}}{40.96 \times 10^{12}} = 0.98 \times 10 = 9.8$$

But 9.8 *what?*

To be quite certain, we figure out the units in the same way:

g must be measured in $\dfrac{\text{m}^3\text{kg}^{-1}\text{s}^{-2} \times \text{kg}}{\text{m}^2} = \text{m s}^{-2}$

In other words, *g* is measured in meters per second per second, which is as it should be, for *g* is an acceleration. Thus we come out with 9.8 m s^{-2}, which is roughly the average or typical gravitational acceleration at Earth's surface. This confirmation reassures us that with *G,* despite its seemingly infinitesimal numerical size, we are on solid ground. *G,* in short, works out correctly— at least here at home, on Earth.

From force to work and energy—Lift a weight a measured distance against the downward pull of Earth's gravitational attraction. As you raise the weight, you do work. The greater the weight, the greater the work required to raise it a certain distance. And for like weights, the greater the distance raised, the greater the work done.

Weight is simply what we call downward force due to gravitation. The *downward* aspect is important, for force, like acceleration, velocity, and even length, is the kind of physical variable in which direction is an essential consideration. Two forces can be added, or subtracted, only by methods that take into account their relative directions as well as their separate magnitudes. This applies also to the addition or subtraction of accelerations, velocities, and lengths. Masses, however, can be added or subtracted without considering "direction." So can volumes and areas.

Now, when motion takes place in a direction opposed by a force, work is always done. The common measure of that work is the size of the force times the distance moved against it. When we raise a 10-pound weight by 6 feet, we do 10 times 6 equals 60 foot-pounds of work.

In the units provided by the great International System, the unit combination to measure work is the meter-newton, or newton-meter. It has its own name—the joule (J) in honor of the great English experimental physicist James Prescott Joule (1818–1889), who measured the mechanical, or energy, equivalent of heat itself.

The joule is the unit to measure work or, as it is more widely known, energy. Energy, like mass, is a variable in which "direction" is not involved. Energies can be added or subtracted without considering the geometry of their "directions."

Energy has indeed become the central variable in science. Every physical interaction and process involves energy equivalents. They may be measured in units of the joule, or in some other unit readily convertible into the joule, such as the electron volt (eV), so important to nuclear and high-energy physics. 1 eV equals 1.60210×10^{-19} J. We have already mentioned in the foreword that 1 watt (of power) during 1 second amounts to 1 joule of energy.

Since energy and its joule unit are so basic to all kinds of physical interactions — mechanical, electrical, molecular, atomic, and nuclear — would it not also have a role in the measurements of gravitational effects? It does, and a most important one.

The second equation, mentioned earlier, showed us gravitation *force* in terms of two masses and the distance between them:

$$F_{grav} = \frac{GM_1M_2}{D^2}$$

That gives us a force (or "weight") measured in units of the newton. But a force times a distance results in work, or an energy, measured in units of the joule. What happens if we multiply both sides of this equation by another distance D? On the left we shall get energy, symbolized by E_{grav} — the subscript reminding us that it is gravitational energy, rather than electrical, chemical, or some other kind. On the right side, the D added in the numerator will have the effect of changing the denominator from D^2 to D. And so the new equation becomes:

$$E_{grav} = \frac{GM_1M_2}{D} \qquad (7)$$

How can we extract energy from a gravitational relationship? It is really quite simple and familiar (Figure 3-2). Here M_1 and M_2 are two massive bodies, their centers at a distance D. We can allow one to fall toward the other, thus decreasing D. As this happens, work is done, such as turning an electric generator by means of a rope. Energy has been emitted, or extracted, gravitationally.

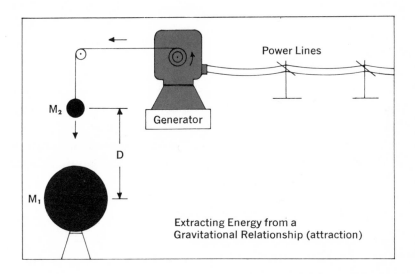

Figure 3-2. As movable mass M_2 drops toward fixed mass M_1 it spins the generator, and the resulting current can do work elsewhere. As the two masses come closer, the "potential energy" that M_2 had because of its distance from M_1, is diminished; and by a like amount the (negative) "binding energy" between M_1 and M_2 grows to greater numerical value.

We could reverse the processes taking place here. If electrical energy (current) is supplied from outside, and the generator operates as a motor to raise M_2 further from M_1, then the (negative) binding energy between M_1 and M_2 diminishes to a smaller numerical value. The energy-changes take place in the opposite direction, but to a like extent—except for losses due to friction and electrical resistances.

When the separation D is large, there is a greater distance through which one mass can fall toward the other, hence more extractable, or "potential" gravitational energy. When D is small, there is less potential gravitational energy, even though the gravitational *force* between the two bodies is greater, in conformity with the effect of D^2 in the denominator of the equation for F_{grav}.

One simple addition should be made to equation (7) in order to escape confusions in the bookkeeping of gravitational energies. A minus sign is inserted before the right-hand side of the equation:

$$E_{grav} = -\frac{GM_1M_2}{D} \qquad (8)$$

This tells us that though the numerical magnitude of the energy grows as D diminishes, it grows in a negative way. In short, as D dwindles, energy (E_{grav}) is emitted. And in order to increase D—to move M_1 and M_2 farther apart—energy has to be supplied from the outside. That is, work must be done. A shrinkage of D is an energy-emitting event; an increase of D is an energy-absorbing event.

Suppose that M_1 and M_2 are enormously far apart. Then D will be so large that the numerical value of E_{grav} will be low—almost zero. But when M_1 and M_2 are quite close, D is small, and E_{grav} is large, in the minus direction. Between the "before" of an enormous D and the "after" of a tiny one, lies the difference—all the energy emitted, or work done, on the way. Perhaps none of this energy actually has been converted into work en route. Then it accumulates in the increasing motion-energy of the masses as they fall together.

The negative energy of equation (8) is often called "the binding energy" or "the gravitational self-energy" of the combination of masses M_1 and M_2. If they come completely together, forming a single lump M_3 then that binding or self-energy can be calculated from:

$$E_{grav} = -\frac{GM^2}{R} \qquad (9)$$

Here the M is the mass of the single body—the M_3 mass mentioned above: and in place of a separation distance D we have another distance R, the radius of the sphere in which the mass is contained.

The greater the negative magnitude of the gravitational binding energy, as measured by equations (8) and (9), the greater the work that must be done—or energy expended—to pull apart the bits of matter, large or small, that are thus bound gravitationally. The falling together of bodies under gravitational influence sets free surprisingly large amounts of energy per unit of mass taking part in the process.

Enter gravitational potential, ϕ—Equations (2) and (8) for gravitational force and energy, respectively, have this in common: each includes two separate masses, M_1 and M_2. We showed that by eliminating the minor mass M_2 from the force equation, we obtained the equation (3) for gravitational *acceleration:* $g = GM_1/D^2$. This acceleration, measured in units of m s^{-2}, will prevail for *any* body located at distance D from the mass-center of M_1. This acceleration is, so to speak, the "force per unit mass" found at distance D from M_1.

Is there a corresponding way to use equation (8)? Can we eliminate from it the minor mass M_2 and get something describable as the "energy per unit mass" found at distance D from M_1? That something is, in fact, very important in the study of gravitation. It is given the name "gravitational potential," and is commonly symbolized by the Greek letter phi: ø. Its recipe, or equation, is quite simple:

$$\phi = -\ \frac{GM}{D} \tag{10}$$

Once again the minus sign is necessary for good bookkeeping of gravitational effects.

Gravitational energy, like all energy, is measured in units of the joule, 1 joule being equal to 1 m^2 kg s^{-2}. Gravitational potential, as just shown, is gravitational energy divided by unit mass. Hence the kg, unit of measure for mass, must vanish from that unit combination; and the unit combination for measuring gravitational potential ø becomes just $m^2 s^{-2}$, or in words "meters squared per second squared." Suppose we write that unit combination in a different, but equivalent form, as $(m\ s^{-1})^2$. That still means $m^2\ s^{-2}$, but now we can see that it is the same, in unit terms, as a velocity $(m\ s^{-1})$ squared. Somehow gravitational potential is measured as if it were, or were akin to, the square of a velocity.

We shall see that it is related in a curious way with that most basic and ultimate of all velocities c, the velocity of light in empty space, measured at very nearly 3×10^8 m s^{-1}.

G as grand marshall of the gravitational procession—Now we have passed in review four basic recipes, or equations, for measuring gravitational effects. (See equations numbers (2), (3), (8), and (10) for gravitational force, acceleration, energy, and potential, respectively.) Each of the four can be rearranged to provide a different definition of the one great gravitational constant G:

$$G = \frac{F_{grav}\ D^2}{M_1 M_2} = \frac{gD^2}{M_1} = -\ \frac{E_{grav}\ D}{M_1 M_2} = -\ \frac{\phi D}{M_1}$$

(Force) (Acceleration) (Energy)   (Potential)

M_2, when it appears alone, usually represents the mass of some major central body, such as the Sun or the Earth. What constitutes a major mass and what a minor mass is, of course, quite relative, gravitationally speaking. Thus, for the Earth the Sun is a major mass; for the Moon the Earth is a major mass; while the Moon becomes the major mass for a space vehicle in orbit around it; and so on.

We see how G is a common link between all four of these basic equations. They are related, but separate, tools for gravitational analysis. Each yields results expressed in units appropriate to it—force in newtons; acceleration in m s^{-2}, energy in joules, potential (ϕ) in m^2 s^{-2}.

A two by two display of these four tools helps more clearly to emphasize their likenesses and differences:

       (A)   (B)

ACCELERATION (LT^{-2})   FORCE (LMT^{-2})

$$g = \frac{GM^1}{D^2} \qquad\qquad F_{grav} = \frac{GM_1M_2}{D^2}$$

       (C)   (D)

POTENTIAL (L^{2}T^{-2})   ENERGY (L^{2}MT^{-2})

$$\phi = -\frac{GM_1}{D} \qquad\qquad E_{grav} = -\frac{GM_1M_2}{D}$$

The top row (acceleration and force) are variables in which direction as well as magnitude matter. They can be combined only when those directions are properly taken into account. The bottom row (potential and energy) have magnitude only, not direction. They represent conditions or relations in the space surrounding the body designated by M_1. Both require the minus sign as guide to proper interpretation.

The variables at left (acceleration and potential) make use only of the mass of the major body (M_1), the need to use the particular mass of some responding body (M_2) having been eliminated. Hence the two equations at left apply to conditions affecting each body in the indicated region of space around M_1.

Gravitation and gradients—One more significant relation exists: between each item above and the one just below it, that is between acceleration and potential; and between force and energy. The upper equation, in each case, acts like the slope or "gradient" of the physical situation measured by the equation just below it.

Figure 3-3 shows an imaginary contour map, such as geologists might make to show heights and slopes in a region. The lines are curves connecting points of equal altitude. At the center is shown a peak 1000 m high. Every ring around that peak indicates a drop of 10 m in altitude. Hence, any movement that crosses ten such lines in any direction, represents a loss of 100 m in altitude. The scale of this map is 10,000 to 1, so 1 cm on the map corresponds to 100 m in the real terrain.

Any single point on a curved line of this map has a magnitude—its altitude above sea-level in meters. But these points have no direction. They are like the gravitational variables of potential and energy in this respect.

However, if, from the map, we seek to find the steepest slopes or gradients, or the least steep slopes or gradients, then we have to define them both by degree (magnitude) of slope and by direction (in terms of compass points). In this respect they are like the gravitational variables of acceleration and force.

Suppose we start from the summit and move due north toward A, as shown on our map. Then we lose 100 m altitude with a northward shift of 275 m. We can call the average slope along that route 100/275, or 0.364. If we move northeast toward B, we find an average slope of 0.133; and eastward, toward C,

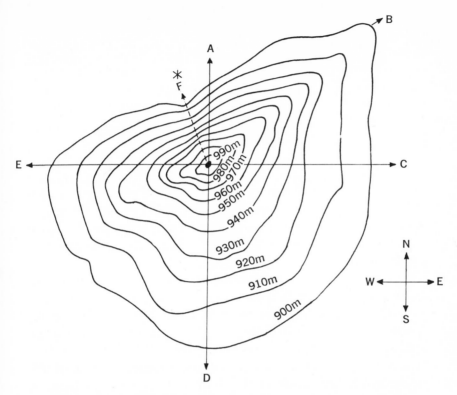

Figure 3-3. Gradients or slopes have direction, whether on a contour map like this one, or in gravitational relations. Gravitational acceleration (g) is the "gradient" of gravitational potential (ϕ). Gravitational force (F_{grav}) is the "gradient" of gravitational energy (E_{grav}). When we measure ϕ or E_{grav} we deal in magnitudes only; but when we describe acceleration (g) or force (F_{grav}) we need to include *direction* as well as magnitude. The latter two are vector variables; the former two are scalar variables. They must be handled accordingly when they are being combined, that, is, when they are being added or subtracted.

the average slope is 0.148, while southward, toward D, it is 0.182.

But we can see that the contour lines are most crowded in the northwesterly direction, toward F. In that direction we find an average slope of 0.444—the largest gradient of all.

Suppose we think of the lines on this map as marking equal gravitational potentials (ϕ) around some central body M_1—a rather unsymmetrical one, this time. The levels now have negative values, such as $-990, -980, -970$, and so on, as we move away from the central body, or peak of (minus) potential. In what direction will the gravitational acceleration be greatest? Obviously in the direction from F toward the central body, for here lies the steepest potential gradient. Acceleration is, in a sense, simply a measure of the gradient or slope of the gravitational potentials around a central body.

Let us now think of the lines on the map as marking locations of equal gravitational *energies*. Again the minus signs must be used with the magnitudes. Now the various slopes or gradients leading to the central body (at the peak) represent the forces which seem to impell minor bodies (the M_2 bodies) toward that central one. The steeper a slope, the greater the force.

So acceleration indicates the rate of change per distance moved toward the attracting body, of the gravitational potentials. And force indicates the rate of change per distance moved toward the attracting body, of the gravitational energies.

Gravitational "contour maps" like this one could be drawn for small masses as well as large, for just as every great M_1 in the universe attracts every little M_2 everywhere, so too does each M_2 attract every M_1. And if we consider only one M_1 and one M_2, then the former attracts the latter with precisely the same force as the latter attracts the former. The pull of the Earth on the Moon is no less and no more than that of the Moon on the Earth.

Action and reaction, as Newton told the world, are everywhere equal but in opposite directions. As the Lincolnshire apple fell toward the ground, so too, though to a far lesser extent, did that ground and all the Earth with it move upward to meet that falling apple.

It is only the enormously greater mass of the Earth relative to the apple, or of the Earth to a falling meteorite, that permits us the fiction of figuring as if the Earth remains "motionless" while apple or meteorite do all the accelerating.

4

Alternative Orbits
and Gravitational Intensities

The great gravitational constant G serves also in equations that permit us to chart possible orbits and flight paths around any planet or star, once we know that body's mass and its size as a sphere.

Calculations of required velocities are important at the outset, for only by attaining such velocities at the proper time and place in space can man-made vehicles, with or without astronauts inside, establish desired orbits, or break free of one such orbit to enter another.

We begin with a spherical body whose mass M we know. What orbital velocity V_o must be attained and maintained by a satellite to orbit in a circle at distance D from the center of M? The circular orbit is the simplest possible one, for it maintains an unchanging velocity as well as an unchanging D at all times.

We have seen, equation (10), that gravitational potential $\phi = -GM_1/D$. Potential ϕ is measured in units of $m^2\ s^{-2}$, like the square of a velocity, measured in $m\ s^{-1}$. And, in fact, the square of the velocity of a body in circular orbit corresponds to the gravitational potential (ϕ) which is found uniformly around that orbit:

$$V_o{}^2 = \frac{GM_1}{D} \tag{11}$$

The minus sign is not needed in that case. This square of the circular orbital velocity corresponds exactly to the gravitational energy that each unit mass (1 kg) possesses at this distance from the center of the orbited body. Also, the circular orbital velocity equals the square root of the gravitational potential around that orbit:

$$V_O = (\phi)^{1/2} = \left(\frac{GM_1}{D}\right)^{1/2} \tag{12}$$

This shows that the velocity necessary for circular orbit diminishes in inverse proportion to the square root of the orbital distance D. If D is increased fourfold, V_O is reduced by half. If D goes up nine times, V_O drops to a third. And so on.

How can we predict the period T_O required for a full rotation in circular orbit? The equation that describes this is simpler than it may appear at first sight:

$$T_O{}^2 = \frac{4\pi^2 D^3}{GM_1} \tag{13}$$

Which means that:

$$T_O = \left(\frac{2\pi D^3}{GM}\right)^{1/2} \tag{14}$$

For any particular spherical body of mass M_1, the period of circular orbit T_O is related to the radius of rotation D by this simple pattern:

$$\frac{T_O{}^2}{D^3} = \text{a constant} \tag{15}$$

This is just the relationship that Johannes Kepler derived from his measurements of the motions of the planets which he knew circled the Sun. He offered it to the world as his Third Law.

Suppose now that we wish a satellite to go into a circular orbit of a certain period T_0 which we have selected in advance. How do we find the distance D at which the satellite must revolve around its central body? That answer takes the form of a related equation:

$$D = \left(\frac{T_0 GM}{4\pi^2}\right)^{1/3} \tag{16}$$

The exponent $\frac{1}{3}$ tells us to take the "cube root" of the amount inside the parentheses.

Seemingly stationary satellites in the sky—Suppose we have decided to orbit a satellite that shall circle the Earth just as often as the Earth itself turns, which is once every 86,160 seconds, relative to the "fixed stars." This is, in fact, a so-called SYNCOM satellite, which, when it orbits in the plane of the Equator, seems to hang motionless in space over some spot on that Equator.

Equation (16) informs us that such a satellite should circle at a height of 35,786,000 meters above Earth's surface. This, when added to the Earth's own radius of about 6,390,000 meters, produces the correct D for that particular orbital period. Synchronous orbiting of Earth is thus accomplished at a D of about 6.6 times Earth's own average radius.

This feat of maintaining a seemingly fixed position in space has been accomplished with such communications satellites as *Early Bird,* and is striking evidence of the practical usefulness of the tools supplied by Newtonian gravitational analysis—for each significant equation is, in fact, a tool.

Energies in orbit—Every speeding mass has energy resulting from its motion. Called "kinetic" or "mechanical" energy, this energy is proportional both to the mass of the moving body and to the square of its velocity. The equation, in fact, is:

$$E_{kin} = \frac{MV^2}{2} \tag{17}$$

Equation (12) has shown that velocity in circular orbit is related to M, the mass of the central body, and D, the distance from its center, in this way: $V_o = (GM_1/D)^{1/2}$. If we square both sides, we get $V_o^2 = GM_1/D$. And we know now from equation (17) that the kinetic energy of the orbiting body equals the square of its orbital velocity times its mass, divided by 2. Substituting GM_1/D for the V^2 in equation (17), we get $E_{kin} = GM_1/D \times M_2/2$ which can be rewritten as this elegant recipe for the energy of a body M_2 in orbit around a body of mass M_1:

$$E_{orb} = \frac{GM_1M_2}{2D} \tag{18}$$

But beside this energy that M_2 has as a result of its orbital motion, there is still that other energy—the binding or gravitational energy between M_2 and M_1 at distance D. That energy has already been measured by equation (8):

$$E_{grav} = -\frac{GM_1M_2}{D}$$

Thus we see that the orbital energy is positive and numerically equal to one half the negative binding energy. This is a simple, significant relationship. It is easy to see that the orbital energy must be positive, for the circling satellite could bump into another and impart to it some of its kinetic energy. The binding or gravitational energy is negative, for work would have to be done on or to that satellite to move it a distance greater than D from the central body M_1.

Kinetic energy can be compared with a kind of wealth belonging to the orbiting body. The binding, or gravitational, energy, however, is like a debt that the satellite owes the central body, and vice versa. So long as that debt is greater than the wealth, the satellite cannot pay off that debt and get free of the central body. In past centuries indentured servants were obliged to work for their masters until they had paid off a stipulated sum. So it is with bodies moving in orbit around others.

Let us examine the energy accounts. Any satellite in circular orbit has, as its asset, a kinetic energy of $GM_1M_2/2D$, and as its liability or debt the binding (gravitational) energy of $-GM_1M_2/D$. Hence the satellite's debt is double the size of its assets or wealth. In every circular orbiting satellite there is a *net deficiency* of energy to the amount of $GM_1M_2/2D$. The positive kinetic energy is only half as large, numerically, as the negative binding energy. This is a simple relationship, and should not be difficult to remember.

We have seen that if we increase by just 1.414 or $(2)^{1/2}$ the velocity of any satellite in circular orbit, the satellite reaches escape velocity. That increase is exactly the one which will *double* the satellite's kinetic energy, raising it to the same (positive) numerical level as the (negative) numerical level of the binding energy.

The negative, then, exactly offsets the positive. The net energy is, in fact, zero. Nothing more than the binding energy ties the satellite to the rule (gravitational) of the central body. A critical point is thus reached.

All these changes have their geometrical effects in the altered shapes of the orbits. As velocity rises beyond that of circular orbit, the orbit lengthens out, becoming an ellipse, or rather an endless series of ever-lengthening ellipses. The length of the longer axis of the ellipse becomes twice, three times, four times, and so on, that of the shorter.

Finally, when 1.414 times V_o is attained, the drawn-out ellipse simply opens; it ceases to be a closed figure. The satellite is off now, on one arm of a parabola. It has escaped (Figure 4-1).

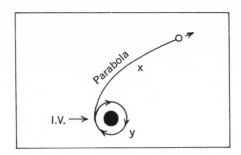

Figure 4-1. A satellite has here been orbiting uniformly in a circle around a central body, shown in black at the center. At the point marked I.V., for "increase of velocity," its velocity is increased by jet action to 1.414 times the previous amount. Its circular orbit is changed to one arm of a *parabola* which it now follows on a nonreturning course into space—where it may later be captured by another massive body, and may once again fall into a bound orbit.

If V_o has been raised beyond 1.414 times, the escape of the satellite follows one arm of a hyperbola. The kind of hyperbola depends on how far the 1.414 velocity has been exceeded (Figure 4-2).

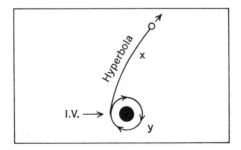

Figure 4-2. A still speedier escape. This satellite has also been orbiting around the central body, shown in black. At the point marked I.V., again for "increase in velocity," the satellite is accelerated by jet action to *more than* 1.414 times its previous velocity in orbit. It leaves the circular orbit and takes off on one arm of a hyperbola, as shown. It too may later be captured by another massive body, and fall into a bound orbit—probably an elliptical one.

All of the curves thus far mentioned for orbits and escape trajectories are members of the famous family of conic sections: the circle (simplest of all ellipses); the ellipses themselves; the parabola; and the hyperbola.

An "escaped" satellite may, of course, be captured later by a more massive body, such as the Sun, or the planet Jupiter. Once again, as the satellite begins to orbit its new gravitational "master," we can be certain that the new debt of binding energy exceeds the satellite's wealth of kinetic or motion energy. The escape velocity that permits a satellite to run free of the Earth will be far less than is needed to permit its escape from the more massive Sun.

The gravitational game of altering orbits—Kinetic energy is just half as large as binding energy in all circular orbits. The two are just equal for the slowest possible escape trajectory. Between these ratios of 50 percent and 100 percent lie all the other possibilities, each corresponding to an orbit of some particular degree of eccentricity, or "ellipticity." Thanks to this fact, it is possible to shift a satellite from one circular orbit to another, or, for that matter, from one elliptical orbit to another. The changes are effected by altering the velocity of the satellite as it orbits, using its jets to accelerate it to greater speed, or—sometimes—by using retrojets to decelerate it and reduce its orbital velocity.

Astronauts thus do not "steer" their spacecraft in the sense that a motorist steers his car on a broad highway or an aviator steers his plane in Earth's lower atmosphere. Rather, the men who navigate space do so essentially by exchanging, or shifting, orbits. They play a game requiring skill and planning, using the possible relationships between the (a) kinetic, and (b) gravitational or binding energies of their vehicles.

For example: we are in circular orbit around Earth at distance D from its center. We wish, however, to move out to another circular orbit, at a distance of just 4 D. We know what D is in meters, what our mass is in kilograms, what the mass of the Earth is, and the magnitude of the constant G.

For simplicity, let us represent our present kinetic energy by an index number of 100. That means that the gravitational binding energy is just -200, and that the difference or deficit of -100 units is holding us in this circular orbit around Earth.

To elongate that circle into an ellipse that will swing us out just far enough, we turn on our jets for a time sufficient to add just 60 units of kinetic energy to our previous 100. This means we accelerate to a velocity about 26.5 percent greater than the previous velocity.

Our kinetic energy is now not 50 percent of our binding energy, but 80 percent. Accordingly, our orbit is now an ellipse with the Earth's center at one focus. We swing out until, at the opposite side of this new elliptical orbit, we find ourselves 4 times more distant than before from Earth's center.

This long "climb" away from Earth has reduced our velocity to a quarter of what it was when we left the first circular orbit. We have remaining only 10 units of kinetic energy, but we are at a distance from Earth that requires 25 such units if we are to remain in circular orbit and not "drop" back earthward in our elliptical orbit. Hence, we supply 15 additional units of kinetic energy by again firing our jet toward the rear. This gives us just the needed 25 units of kinetic energy.

As we coast onward, following a fully circular orbit now, at a distance from earth four times that at which we began, we can cast up our accounts, energetically speaking. Our present binding energy of -50 units holds us in the new orbit, for we now have an energy deficit of 25 units. At the start, that deficit was 100 units. We have reduced that deficit by 75 units during our maneuvers.

From where did that difference of 75 energy units come? From the two blasts of our jet engine. First, 60 units of energy were added to take us from our initial circular orbit into the desired elliptical swing outward. Then, when we had attained a maximum on that path, we added 15 energy units more to regain a circular orbit at a distance four times greater than before from Earth's center.

The energy accounts must always balance. They include the positive "assets" or kinetic energy of motion; and the minus, or liability, entries for gravitational binding energy: and such deposits or withdrawals as the changes that take place in each type of energy. Freedom to shift from orbit to orbit depends on ability to add kinetic energy, or reduce kinetic energy, by using jet thrusts (forces) as they are needed.

It would be possible to reverse our maneuver and drop down from a more distant to a closer orbit. To do that we should have to *de*celerate by firing a jet toward the direction in which we are orbiting. By thus reducing our 25 kinetic energy units to 10, we would be in an elliptical orbit again, travelling now in the reverse track of that which led us from the 1 D to the 4 D circular orbit.

When we reached the lowest point in that ellipse, before starting to swing away again from Earth, we would once more use our retrojet. We would need to slow down in order to cut our 160 kinetic energy units back to the 100 that permit us to orbit in a circle at that 1 D distance.

Obviously, dependable thrust engines and the fuel to supply them are essential to space travel, whether such travel is around Earth only, or includes far ranging flights from the Earth to the Moon, to Mars, or to other planets.

Two cautions must be observed in these fascinating games of shifting from orbit to orbit. When adding velocity beyond that of the circular orbit, do not accelerate to 1.414 times the former speed—unless you wish to follow an "escape" trajectory and never return to Earth. Also, when decelerating from the velocity of a circular orbit, make sure the new ellipse does not intersect the surface of Earth itself—unless you wish to "land" and are well provided against the heating effects of a swift passage through the lower atmosphere.

Vital velocities in gravitational study—For every massive central body, such as Sun, Earth, or Moon, there are two velocities of special importance gravitationally. Both are involved with relationships that exist at the surface of the body. The first is the escape velocity at the surface of the body, V_E. The other, which can be symbolized by V_{so}, is the velocity of a circular orbit that exists just at the surface of the massive central body. Because of atmospheres and other surface problems, both V_E and V_{so} are more useful in calculations than they are likely to be observed in action.

For Earth, V_{so} is about 7.9×10^3 m s⁻¹. Since escape velocity is just 1.414 times circular orbit velocity, V_E at Earth's surface is just over 11×10^3 m s⁻¹. Such high velocities are blocked by the atmospheric resistance at the surface of Earth.

Our Sun, a moderately massive star, contains about 2×10^{30} kg of mass within its radius of about $7b$ 10^8 m. Its V_{so} is 4.36×10^5 m s⁻¹ and its V_E is about 6.2×10^5 m s⁻¹. Both V_{so} and V_E are related simply and "elegantly"—as scientists like to say—to the gravitational potential ϕ which prevails where they are measured. V_{so} always equals $(\phi)^{1/2}$, which means that it is also equal to $(GM/D)^{1/2}$. V_E, for its part, is equal always to $(2\,\phi)^{1/2}$, and so to $(2\,GM/D)^{1/2}$.

Gravitational potential ϕ, as already noted, is closely identified with the square of a velocity and is measured in the same units as a velocity squared: that is, m² s⁻².

Einstein's relativity theories showed that gravitation itself and every other kind of energy relationship is intimately linked with one more velocity—an invariable, universal "speed limit." It is c, the velocity of light and all electromagnetic radiations, when they move through "empty space." Its precise value is very nearly 299,792,500 m s⁻¹, usually rounded to an even 3×10^8 m s⁻¹.

Relativity does *not* show that all physical relations are relative, for c is an absolute. Every observer, no matter what his velocity or direction of motion, will find the same value for c that we do. Nowhere in the universe can energy, or matter, or information be transmitted at a rate to exceed c. Even gravitation and its effects travel through space at c, just as do waves of light and radio. This great cosmic constant c provides us with a standard for judging whether other velocities and physical effects are "small," "medium," or "large" in magnitude.

Escape velocity V_E at the Sun's surface is about $c/500$. Hence we can consider the Sun, despite its vastness compared to Earth, as having a small or low gravitational intensity at its surface. This could be concluded, for the same reasons, with regard to a large proportion of the myriads of stars in galaxies throughout space. The Sun is fairly representative of a large number of stars, gravitationally speaking. But not of *all* the stars, by any means.

With some surprise, astronomers learned many decades ago that there exist large numbers of "old" stars whose masses are as great as the Sun's or even greater, but which have shrunk to sizes similar to that or our little Earth!

Such stars are called *dwarfs*. They represent an advanced stage in stellar aging. Once they were more or less sunlike in density. But now, as their inner nuclear fuel is consumed, they contract. First they become luminous "white dwarfs." Then gradually they cool further and darken out of sight. Such is their end, as it was first conceived by astronomers and physicists.

Dwarfs in size, monsters in density—Water's density supplies us with a standard measurement. It is the unit for "specific gravity." Earth's average density represents a "specific gravity" of about 5.3. The Sun's is far less—only about 1.4, even though the hot, compressed matter in its central core is vastly denser than that average.

The white dwarf stars, however, must have average densities of about 15 to 17 *million* times that of water. With so much matter jammed, by gravitational force, into so small a volume the result is huge gravitational potentials (ϕ) at their surfaces, and in space nearby. V_E for a typical dwarf star is probably about 6×10^6 m s^{-1}, if not more. That is more than 2 percent of c. We are beginning to reach the realm of "medium"-sized gravitational intensities, as viewed by relativity.

During recent years the evidence has increased, rapidly and astoundingly, that even such dense dwarfs may be far less dense and less potent, gravitationally, than other great bodies in our universe. The existence of such bodies was not dreamed of until a very few decades ago.

These stars are given such names as super-dense dwarfs, neutron stars, gravitationally collapsed stars, Schwarzschild singularities, and sometimes they are identified with pulsars, with quasi-stellar objects or quasars, and with a variety of strange suppositions and conjectures.

With these objects, so different from the concepts of the recent past, we enter the realm of really "high" gravitational effects, as measured by the invariable standard of c itself.

5

Approaching the Ultimate

Is there no limit to possible gravitational intensity?

There is such a limit, contained in Einstein's general relativity theory. This limit is related, significantly, with c, the invariable velocity of light in space, which is measured in units of meters per second (m s^{-1}) like any speed.

We have seen that gravitational potential $\emptyset$ is measured in units which are those of a velocity *squared* (m^2 s^{-2}, which is the same as the square of m s^{-1}).

General relativity theory indicates that we shall never observe any object anywhere, whose surface escape velocity V_E is greater than c itself. What is the nature of a mass M whose escape velocity has climbed to this cosmic limit? It must be so shrunken or compacted that its radius R_s has a particular relationship to its mass M:

$$R_s = \frac{M \times 2G}{c^2} \quad \text{or} \quad \frac{R_s}{M} = \frac{2G}{c^2}$$

That constant proportion, $2\ G/c^2$, is extremely tiny. It is, in fact, just about 1.5×10^{27} m kg^{-1} (meters per kg). To reach that critical limit, our Earth would have to shrink to a radius (R_s) of about 0.004 meters (4 mm !). And even the great mass of our Sun would have to be packed into a sphere of only 3×10^3 (3 km) radius, to reach this limit!

The radius of such a mass is represented commonly with the

subscript s (R_s) and called "the Schwarzschild radius." That name recalls Karl Schwarzschild (1873–1961), an able German astronomer and mathematician. In the very year of his death, he made important contributions to general relativity theory, just after the theory was first published by Einstein.

It is not possible to regard this ultimate size R_s as if it were an ordinary length. The intense gravitational field around a mass so dense and shrunken warps the structure of space-time. Though our common concepts of length break down under these extreme conditions, we can recall that R_s represents the size-to-mass relationship of a body gravitating so intensely that nothing can ever leave it to reach any other part of the universe. Neither radiations nor matter can escape from such an ultimately shrunken body, for its escape velocity has risen to c, the universal "speed limit."

There is another "relativistic" length sometimes called the "gravitational length" or "gravitational radius" of a mass M. It is symbolized sometimes by M*, to indicate that it is the geometrical or length equivalent of a mass. The equation for it is $M^* = GM/c^2$. Hence its value is just half that of the R_s for the same mass.

Light, too, gravitates — Light behaves as if it were emitted and absorbed in tiny energy packets, which Einstein named "photons." The higher the frequency (f) of the light, the larger the energy in its particular photon "packets." Thus a violet photon represents almost twice the energy of a red photon.

But relativity shows that where there is energy, there is also mass, or the equivalent of mass. Work is required to lift a mass against gravitational pull. To radiate light against the pull of gravitation requires work too, and this work, or energy, is deducted from the energy content of photons as they fly out from the emitting body.

Hence, light emitted from a surface with high gravitational potential and received on one of low gravitational potential has lost energy. Its photons, consequently, appear redder, or appear shifted in frequency toward the red.

Gravitational potential ϕ is so low here on Earth that we can regard it as zero when compared with that at the surface of great stars, especially at the surface of the shrunken dwarf stars.

Einstein supplied an equation that shows the extent of the frequency shifting or "reddening" that should be observed with varying gravitational potentials at the emitting and receiving sites. We deal here with stars whose size is greater than that at their R_s or Schwarzschild radius—for no light can leave a star once the star has shrunk *that* far.

We represent by f_o the frequency we observe when the light from a star is received on Earth, and by f_n the frequency of light emitted by the same atomic processes when they take place here on Earth itself. Then, if ϕ is the gravitational potential at that star's surface, we should find the following relation between the observed frequency and the normal frequency of the light:

$$\frac{f_o}{f_n} = \left(\frac{1 - 2\phi}{c^2}\right)^{1/2} \qquad (19)$$

The exponent $\frac{1}{2}$ means, as always, "take the square root of" what is inside the parentheses.

We have seen earlier, from equation (10), that the gravitational potential has this relationship to the mass M and radius R of the body involved: $\phi = GM/R$. (The minus sign can be overlooked here). Substituting that fraction for the ϕ in equation (19), we get:

$$\frac{f_o}{f_n} = \left(1 - \frac{2GM}{c^2 R}\right)^{1/2} \qquad (20)$$

That same significant combination, $2\,GM/c^2$, appeared also in the equation for the Schwarzschild radius R_s of any mass M.

As a test, let us see what happens if, in equation (20), we make the R equal to the Schwarzschild radius R_s for that star of mass M. We find that the amount inside the parentheses becomes $1-1=0$. That means that $f_o/f_n=0$. The result is that the observed frequency becomes negligible, or zero, compared with the frequency of the same radiation emitted on Earth.

In other words, light—and, indeed, all events—on a body shrunken to that ultimate radius R_s, appear to us on Earth to have been slowed down to a complete halt. The light of such a body has been shifted all the way off the scale of vibrations. We cannot even receive it at radio wavelengths. It cannot be received in any way. Any other physical process seems never to finish—so far as it is visible to earthly observers of the star. Time has been stretched out indefinitely.

Let us see what the Einstein gravitational "reddening" amounts to in cases less extreme than this ultimate one of a "Schwarzschild radius" source. The sun's surface ∅ exceeds that of the Earth enough to produce only a very tiny decrease in the apparent frequency of light from the Sun—about 3 parts in 100,000. This amount is probably too small to be reliably detected. Atmospheric and other effects cause variations that simply swamp any difference so tiny. Even a typical "white dwarf" star should show a frequency loss of only some 4 parts in 10,000, as observed from Earth.

What of a dwarf star that shrank still further—until, to make an example, its radius were only a quarter that of our own small Earth? The star's light, received here, should show a frequency loss of about 0.6 of 1 percent. And if shrinkage continued until that star had only one-twenty-fifth of Earth's radius, the loss of frequency would be about 1 percent.

Estimates of this sort were largely speculations during more than a quarter century after Einstein's general relativity equations first appeared. There was then no observable evidence that gravitational potentials existed that were large enough to show gravitational redshifting of sufficient size to confirm the theory.

However during the last of the 1930s, some theoretical physicists began to envisage events involving great masses of stellar matter undergoing increases in density and gravitational force enormously greater than ever before conjectured.

A pioneer in this direction was J. Robert Oppenheimer, then a leading theoretical physicist at Berkeley. (Not much later he led developmental work on the first nuclear bombs, with consequences so fearful for the world and fateful for his own career and prestige.) In theoretical papers, coauthored with various colleagues, Oppenheimer outlined processes by which "old" stars of sufficient mass, after passing through their "dwarf" stages, might shrink still further in a process of gravitational collapse. According to Oppenheimer, such a star's (negative) binding energy, growing ever greater, could overwhelm every resisting force or effect.

In fact, the process of collapse could—in this view—run all the way to an untraceable end. The collapsing star would shrink not only to but beyond—or rather *inside of*—its Schwarzschild radius. The outside world (universe) would never be able to perceive the stages past the Schwarzschild limit, however.

It became clear that such gravitational collapse would be accompanied by enormous emissions of energy in very short intervals of time—in short, by fantastic outpourings of power.

Today there is widespread and increasing acceptance of the likelihood that such total gravitational collapse does occur. This trend is strengthened by one simple, powerful fact: only gravitational collapse provides the possibility of accounting for extraordinary, but undeniable, observations made in recent years by astronomers, both through optical and radio means.

The peculiar path to total collapse—One may use Einstein's equation (19) to make rough estimates of the frequency loss and time retardation as a body shrinks all the way to its Schwarzschild radius.

The author has done this for seven hypothetical stages passed through by a body using the mass of our Sun—about 2×10^{30} kg. However, a few preliminary cautions should be given.

First, many authorities believe that such complete collapse can take place only with "old" stars whose remaining mass is about 1.5 times, or more, that of the Sun. In fact, some speculations have considered as typical the catastrophic collapses of supposed stellar bodies with a thousand times or more the Sun's mass. Our purpose here, however, is merely to show how rapidly the "redshifting" process accelerates as the Schwarzschild radius is approached in the final stages.

Second, some theorists have calculated that we on Earth cannot expect to observe frequencies of light from stars reduced to less than a certain percentage of "normal." One estimate places that percentage at about 77 percent; another at about 62 percent. Without going into these possibilities, our table shows what percentage of "normal" frequency would be seen by Earth observers, if they could follow all the reddening process to the final total fade-out.

The column at left gives an informal description of the state of the star whose radius R is given in meters in the middle column. At right we see how the Earth-observed frequencies of its light would be reduced, ever more rapidly, as the final "closed system" or Schwarzschild state is approached.

TABLE 1

Kind of Star	Star's Radius, m	Star's Frequencies (Seen from Earth)
(A) "Medium" neutron star	2.5×10^4	94 percent of normal
(B) "Small" neutron star	1.5×10^4	90 percent of normal
(C) Collapsing, 1st stage	7.4×10^3	87 percent of normal
(D) Collapsing, 2nd stage	6×10^3	71 percent of normal
(E) Collapsing, 3rd stage	4.5×10^3	58 percent of normal
(F) Schwarzschild star— "closed system"	3×10^3	0 percent of normal

Gravitational collapse clearly is a "galloping process." As shrinkage approaches the Schwarzschild limit, the redshift effect accelerates. Yet acceleration may not be the best word to use, for as gravitational potential rises on the surface of the collapsing object, to the Earthbound observer the events taking place on the body would seem to occur ever more slowly. Just at, or rather, just before, the Schwarzschild limit was reached, all "transmission" of information as seen from Earth and elsewhere in the universe would draw to a halt. That is the implication of the term "closed system," sometimes used to typify such a collapsed object.

Such a star—or ex-star—is truly in a "black hole." It has, to all intents and purposes, withdrawn from the rest of the universe. Yet its static gravitational attraction should still be felt, even if the source of that gravitation is no longer seen to shine or otherwise transmit energy. It is possible, and even anticipated, that from time to time other stellar objects, or objects of planetary size, might be attracted to this star and fall into that "black hole," where they too would be extinguished for outside observers when they had reached the state of gravitational potential equivalent to an escape velocity of c.

Evidence from Earth—Einstein's prediction of frequency changes in radiation from differing gravitational strengths at emitting and receiving sites, has been impressively confirmed. The evidence did not come from distant space however. It was all done in a tower on Earth, at Harvard University. Two physicists there, R. V. Pound and G. A. Rebka, had realized that the so-called Mössbauer Effect, discovered in the early 1960s, offered a test method of sensitivity beyond anything previously available. They determined to apply it to the action of gravitation on radiation.

Mössbauer, a young German physicist who received the Nobel Prize for his discovery, had found that certain atoms, when locked into crystalline solid structures, could be made to emit gamma rays so precisely uniform that deviations as tiny as one part in a thousand million million could be detected. (1 part in 10^{15}.)

That almost infinitesimal difference was, in fact, even less, by a small amount, than the frequency difference to be expected as a result of the slightly lower gravitational potential at the top of the Jefferson Laboratory Tower at Harvard University, compared with that at the bottom, 73 ft below.

Pound and Rebka used cobalt 57 as an emitter and iron 57 as an absorber of gamma rays, whose energy was 14.4 keV (kilo electron-volts), corresponding to a frequency of about 3.5×10^{18} hertz (cycles per second).

First the emitter was placed at the top of the tower, with the absorber at the base, together with a gamma ray detector to respond to gamma photons that were not absorbed. The photons, in "falling" that 73 ft, should have gained energy sufficient to increase their apparent frequency just under 5 parts in 10^{15}, according to the Einstein equation.

The observed increase in frequency was indeed just about 5.1 parts in 10^{15}. In fact the margin of uncertainty in the test results was greater than the tiny difference between the calculated and the observed effect (Figure 5-1).

Having measured this significant "blue shift" or frequency increase resulting from the photons' fall earthward, Pound and Rebka then reversed their test. They put the emitter at the bottom and the absorber and gamma ray detector at the top of the tower. Thus, as described by Robert L. Forward, a specialist on gravitational research, "they made the poor gamma rays struggle up out of the Earth's gravitational field; hence the rays got weaker and were redshifted when they finally got to the top." Actually, what was measured was the extent to which the iron 57 absorber, a very selective kind of absorbing body, refused to absorb the photons because of the gravity-caused change in their energies, or frequency.

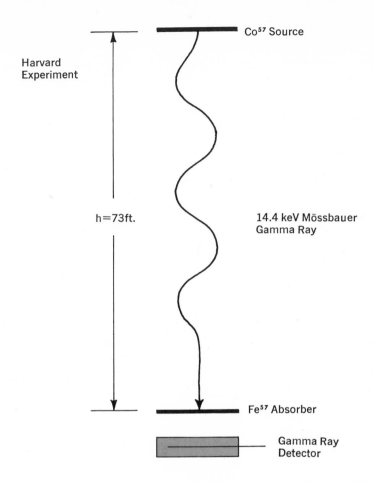

Figure 5-1. A powerful tower-fall test. The difference in gravitational acceleration between the top and bottom of the Jefferson Laboratory tower at Harvard was sufficient, though ultratiny, to be detected by the Mössbauer Effect, as used by physicists Pound and Rebka in the historic experiment here suggested schematically. Gamma rays, emitted by cobalt atoms at the top of the tower, "fell" 73 feet, and in doing so gained energy enough to increase their apparent frequency by about 5 parts in 10^{15}. That minute difference was detected at the bottom, in the form of "extra" gramma photons, which the iron absorber rejected—just because of that slight difference!

In later reruns of this historic Harvard tower experiment, experimenters reduced the deviation between observed and theoretical results to less than 1 percent. A more striking confirmation of a "far out" and seemingly infinitesimal influence of tiny gravitational differences had never previously been attained.

In the history of experimental physics, the Harvard laboratory tower earned a place beside the Leaning Tower of Pisa, from which Galileo either did or did not drop weights to show that bodies fall with the same accelerations whether they are heavier or lighter. The Harvard tower merits a place too with a tower near Paris in which Pascal made an early demonstration that he could use his new barometer as an altimeter. At the top of the tower the mercury in his tube stood lower than at the bottom, thanks to the difference in atmospheric pressures.

In another extraordinary experiment performed at the Argonne Laboratory, Chicago, neutrons from an atomic pile were sorted out so they all moved in a beam in just about the same direction horizontally. Over a path of 180 meters length, the slower neutrons dropped earlier, as a result of gravity, than did the faster ones. A beryllium block acted as filter to let through only the slower ones, which were then "counted" by a neutron detector.

The resulting data showed that the neutrons, tiny though their mass might be, had been following trajectories conforming to the gravitational field through which they "fell" as they moved.

During recent years at Moscow State University in the Soviet Union, Professor Braginski and his associates have completed a series of experiments demonstrating that gravitational "shielding" does not take place. They showed with great precision that the Earth's attraction on a test mass is not reduced by adding matter between the Earth and the test mass.

Such quantitative investigations of the behavior of gravitation are difficult and delicate, for gravitation, under ordinary conditions on Earth, is a very faint and feeble effect. However, the tools and techniques of experimental physics have become more sensitive and precise during the 1950s and 1960s, and we can confidently expect even more penetrating and revealing tests of the assumptions and predictions of general relativity and related theories of gravitation during the 1970s and 1980s. We can, that is, if peace becomes prevalent on Earth, and if the threatening catastrophes of warfare and destruction are avoided.

Helmut K. Wimmer's representation of the black hole. Copyright © 1971 by Helmut K. Wimmer and used by permission.

6

Falling Into Energy

Even before complete gravitational collapse was regarded as a possible process, it was well known that the "falling together" of scattered matter could generate vast amounts of energy, resulting in heat and radiation.

In fact, about a century ago, energy supplied by such gravitational events was suggested as an answer to the stubborn question: how do the Sun and stars continue to shine so long and so brightly?

Two leaders in the attempt to find an answer to this question were a German physician-turned-physicist, Hermann Helmholtz (1821–1894), and the famed Scottish scientist-inventor, William Thomson (1824–1907), better known by his title of Lord Kelvin.

Both Helmholtz and Kelvin were leaders in energetics, the swiftly growing field of physics dealing with the generation and transformations of energy. Together they helped gain acceptance of the principle of the conservation of energy: that energy is only converted from one form to another, never destroyed or created.

Today this principle has been extended, thanks to Einstein's insights. It has become the law of the conservation of mass-energy or energy-mass, for the principle includes the cosmic equivalence law that energy equals mass times the square of the velocity of light ($E = Mc^2$). Since c^2 is synonymous with $9 \times 10^{16} m^2 s^{-2}$, it is clear that a very tiny amount of mass is equivalent to a huge amount of energy and vice versa.

Our Sun is known to radiate energy at a great rate—about 3.7×10^{26} watts, to be exact. This means exactly the same number of joules of energy per second of time. Such enormous outpouring goes on year after year, millenium after millenium. Life on Earth depends on the tiny fraction of this total that is absorbed from this tremendous flood of energy.

Many a star among the myriads in the universe emits power far greater than that of the Sun. What is the source of it all? Helmholtz and Kelvin knew that the source could not be ordinary chemical combustion, such as the combination of carbon with oxygen when coal burns in a furnace on Earth. Even if the Sun's mass had been divided in the right proportions of high-grade coal and pure oxygen, such a "fire" would have supplied its energy output for far too brief a time.

Helmholtz and Kelvin both made computations to see whether the gravitational falling-together or shrinkage of matter in the Sun could account for its long ages of power output. They found that the Sun could have radiated at its present rate for age to present dimensions. However that period was far too brief. Even then there were strong indications that the Sun had radiated as it does now for as long as one billion years. Today the best opinion increases this period to 4 or 5 billion years.

Shrinkage as a source of power—We can use the equation for the (negative) binding energy of gravitation for any single spherical body of whatever mass and radius:

$$E_{grav} = - \frac{GM^2}{R} \tag{21}$$

This means that the energy that was released when widely scattered matter fell together and shrank to the dimensions of the present Sun, must total GM^2/R, M being the Sun's present mass, R its radius.

Each further shrinkage means a further output of energy. Suppose the Sun were to shrink to a third of its present radius. The additional setting-free of energy would be about 7.6×10^{41} joules. That would provide for only about 65 million years of radiation at the Sun's present rate.

Obviously, some mechanism quite different from gravitational compaction and shrinkage of masses of matter must be at work in bodies such as the Sun and most stars, for these bodies shine on through eons and ages with little or no detectable change in dimensions.

That mechanism became apparent some time after Helmholtz and Kelvin's heyday, as the newly discovered world of "radio-activity"—or nuclear processes—was explored.

The mass of all matter is made up almost entirely of the heavy particles known as "nucleons"—protons and neutrons. The surrounding electrons are, comparatively, negligible in their contribution to the total *mass* of the atoms although they are important electrically.

By the 1930s, scientists knew that atomic nuclei were not eternal or unalterable. The component nucleons of these nuclei could be rearranged to form the nuclei of the atoms of other substances, or elements. There were, in fact, two great processes: *fission*—in which a complex nucleus split into simpler ones, each with fewer nucleons; and *fusion*—in which simpler nuclei came together and, eventually, formed fewer and more complex nuclei.

In both of these processes, fission and fusion, the product or "daughter" nuclei were found to contain less total mass than had been in the original, or parent, nuclei. Small but significant amounts of mass thus "disappeared," but not without trace, for they were replaced by equivalent amounts of energy, according to the cosmic law: $E = Mc^2$.

During the late 1930s, several brilliant and persistent nuclear physicists worked out theoretical sequences showing how nuclear fusion processes in the core regions of the Sun and stars could account for the enormous power outpouring of these bodies through long ages. Today there remains no serious doubt that fusion is at work in the heart of the stars, and accounts for their long shining.

The power of such radiation is inevitably accompanied by a loss—or conversion into energy—of equivalent amounts of mass. Our Sun, for example, loses mass at the rate of about $4 \times 10^9 \, \text{kg s}^{-1}$. This is an enormous "wasting away," yet the process would have to go on for more than 10,000 times a billion years before the Sun wasted away to "nothing."

This is, in fact, impossible. The nature of the nuclear processes is such that the "fuel" for fusion is exhausted or becomes unavailable by the time the total loss of mass has attained the level of only 1 or 2 percent.

The first and principle fuel for these fusion "fires" is hydrogen, which is fused or converted to helium. Hydrogen's atomic mass is 1, compared with 4 for helium. However those figures are approximate. The helium nucleus mass is somewhat less than just the total mass of 4 hydrogen nuclei. This difference is the source of the energy of the Sun or star during the hydrogen-to-helium phase which dominates more than 90 percent of the radiative lifetime of a typical star.

The remainder of that star's lifetime derives its energy from the burning of helium nuclei to form nuclei of still heavier elements. Finally, a sort of nuclear barrier is reached in the neighborhood of nuclei of the element iron, with a nuclear mass of about 56 times that of hydrogen, and of about 14 times that of helium. The nuclei of iron and its neighboring elements are especially stable.

From here on, further nuclear transformations require input of energy from the outside rather than a yielding of energy, as in all the fusion transformations up to this point. The "iron stage" means that the inner nuclear fuel is nearly exhausted, and the star faces the changes of "old age."

This great cycle of nuclear burning begins only after gravitational energies raise temperatures high enough in the heart of the young star to kindle the first fusions from hydrogen to helium. The entire long lifetime of a shining star is launched thanks only to the conversion of energies released by gravitational contraction into intense internal heat.

A star is born—Follow the typical life story of a star. We begin with an enormous, diffuse cloud of hydrogen gas and dust scattered through vast reaches of space. Its turbulence creates here and there regions of greater than average density. The gravitational attraction of these areas draws still more matter to them. And so the process snowballs during perhaps 10 to 15 million years.

More and more of the scattered matter falls together in these ever growing clumps. Their centers become heated by the motion-energy of the matter falling inward. Pressures increase, raising temperatures ever higher. Finally, core temperatures reach about 20 million degrees Celsius.

Now the nuclear particles are vibrating with energies high enough to overcome nuclear repulsions. New, more complex nuclei are formed. The stage of thermonuclear reactions has begun. This new outpouring of energy takes place in the stellar core, for only there do temperatures and pressures suffice. Radiation released in the nuclear transformations makes its way slowly through the mass of the star to the surface, and then streams out into space. The star, we would say, has begun to shine.

The total mass of such a new star determines its future life. A mass like that of our Sun has a similar life expectancy, shining by means of thermonuclear fuel consumption for about 10 billion years. A mass much less than the Sun's might never reach the thermonuclear kindling temperature, and so would not attain the status of a star. The universe probably holds bodies that radiate some heat because of their gravitation-generated internal temperature, but that do not shine for lack of full-scale thermonuclear activity at their centers.

Stars with masses far greater than the Sun's, however, would burn through their available hydrogen fuel far faster. Thus, a mass a dozen times that of the Sun might pour out energy at a rate that would cause it to run through its nuclear fuel in a mere 10 million years.

The core temperatures of close to 50 to 100 million degrees that accompany formation of new helium nuclei may seem enormous. But as the star burns on, still higher temperatures will infest its heart. When the helium formation stage gives way to the building of nuclei such as magnesium and calcium, the temperatures are up to about 1 billion degrees. And the end-of-the-line process, resulting in fusion of iron nuclei, goes on amidst core temperature that is about three times higher still.

The typical youth and prime of a star, its period of steady shining through long ages, is marked by a striking equilibrium or balance. The star's rate of radiation and its radius both remain about uniform. The mechanism that maintains this stability is interesting.

Gravitation tries constantly to pull the outer parts of the star inward toward the center. The counterforce is that supplied by the internal release of energy, heat, and—what is the same thing—by the motion of the particles composing the nuclear structures of the star. At any time in a star shining steadily without change in size, there is a balance between those opposing tendencies.

Suppose some contraction were to occur. It would increase both pressure and temperature in the core; that would increase the rate of thermonuclear "burning," and the added energy would expand the star's sphere once again. But not too far.

Not all stars have the stability of size and radiative power now typical of our Sun. Many have reached stages where this self-regulatory process falters and fails. There is a numerous and important group called by astronomers the Cepheid variables. These stars pulsate periodically. Their periods of pulsation are closely related to the power with which they emit light. The "brighter" such a Cepheid, the longer the period of its variation. Some may go from faintest to strongest every 48 hours; others do so in 6 to 8 days; still others need more than 5 or 6 weeks. All such variations are related to the star's stage in the process of consuming the available nuclear fuel within its heart.

But every shining star, sooner or later, must come to the stage where its "burnable" nuclei have been transformed. What follows can be compared to lines the Hungarian poet, Nicolas Lenau, once wrote about Don Juan:

> . . . exhausted is the fuel
> And on the hearth the cold is fiercely cruel.

It is not the mass of the star that has wasted away. Only a tiny fraction of its youthful mass has been converted into the energy of its radiations. But now the remaining mass is made up mostly of nuclear structures that will no longer sustain the thermonuclear processes.

The heat from the heart, which kept the star at or near a certain size, begins to fail. The future of such old stars was suggested by Robinson Jeffers, an American poet with a deep understanding of modern science:

> The heroic stars spending themselves,
> Coining their very flesh into bullets for the lost battle,
> They must burn out at length like used candles . . .
> —from *The Epic Stars,* published 1963

The bullets referred to here were the photons or particles of light and heat radiated while the star converted some of its mass ("flesh") into energy. But the years since Jeffers wrote those lines have brought new and more violent visions of the ends overtaking the most "heroic" stars, that is, those stars with greatest remaining masses, when they reached the end of their nuclear fuel supplies.

The smaller, less heroic stars, with masses less than about 1.4 times that of our Sun, begin shrinking under the influence of their own gravitation as they radiate away more energy than their internal furnaces now supply. This shrinking heats the interior of the star and also keeps the star shining while its radius gets smaller and smaller. The substance of the star becomes denser and denser. Finally, a state is reached where the electrons orbiting the atomic nuclei that now make up the star resist further restriction. They make a "last stand" that sets a limit to the contraction for such sunlike masses. By this time the size has been reduced to a fraction of what it once was. A mass like that of our Sun is now packed into a radius about like that of our Earth.

In these cases of contraction, the internal heat, though huge, dwindles as it is gradually radiated away. The "white dwarf"—the name given to these shrunken old stars—darkens and reddens. Gradually it fades out of sight. It courses through space, a dim, and finally an invisible "cinder." But it does not collapse beyond its already ultradense state, in which—to use our everyday units—each cubic inch of its substance represents a mass of *tons*.

Such is the burning out at length "like used candles," envisaged by Jeffers. It is the fate which ultimately awaits our own Sun, among myriads of other stars now shining steadily in their primes.

Destiny of the giants—What of the stars with masses greater than 1.2 or 1.3 solar masses, when they exhaust their nuclear fuel supplies? Their fates must be more dramatic and more violent. The relative intensity of a star's self-gravitation at any radius goes up as the *square* of its mass. Thus, if a star with 1.5 times the Sun's mass shrank to a dwarf size, with an earthlike radius, its gravitational interaction would be about 2¼ times that of the Sun, shrunken to that same radius.

The resistance of electrons and the remaining internal heat does not suffice to check gravitational shrinkage when the opposing forces are too unbalanced. Two major possibilities have been indicated by the theorists of physics and astronomy.

For stars with masses from about 1.2 or 1.3 times the Sun's

to some uncertain point beyond, the stage following that of "dwarfdom" involves a strange, but plausible transformation of matter in the ultradense interior. The electrons, driven by gravitational pressure, are forced—so to speak—to seek refuge with the nuclear particles from which they have heretofore kept apart. The process is that of the enforced merger of electrons and protons to form neutrons. As this process progresses, the dwarf is transformed into what is commonly called now a "neutron star." Its densities are much higher than those in the dwarf stage. Its substance is essentially a new or different form of matter—not solid, liquid, gas, or plasma. Some scientists speak of a largely "neutronized" star as if it were formed virtually from nuclear matter.

The collapse from dwarf to neutron star stage can be accompanied by gigantic cosmic "catastrophes." Pressures are inevitably greatest in the core, and, there, neutron formation proceeds fastest. Finally, the "neutronized" core collapses; and on the rebound from the center a shock wave is formed. Moving at, or very near, *c,* the velocity of light, this shock wave simply blows off the outer layer of the star.

In these outer layers lingered whatever nuclear fuel had not previously been burned. In this new, most intense reaction, these reserves undergo violent thermonuclear transformations as they are scattered far and wide in space.

Temperatures rising to hundreds of billions of degrees make this new "super-nova" shine as if it were a myriad of stars all rolled into one. Around the shrunken core a wild new radiance lights the heavens.

Super-novas flare up, not often, but unforgettably. Our own galaxy appears to be illuminated by such violent displays of radiation on an average of once each two or three centuries. One of the most famous took place in 1054, and was carefully noted by Chinese astronomers. Today, more than 900 years later, the remnants of that super-nova form the spectacular and extraordinary "Crab Nebula," surrounded by enormous ragged clouds whose tormented shapes tell of their turbulence and velocities. At the heart of that nebula there shines and throbs an especially rapid pulsar. The pulsar is believed to be the remnant of the neutron star that blew off its outer layers to form the nebula, and which shone dominant in the sky during most of a year.

The staggering energies of such super-nova reactions suffice to fuse even iron nuclei to form heavier and more complex elements, and to spread them throughout space—from which they eventually are compacted again into later stars and planets.

Beyond the neutron star—A dwarf star may retain too much mass and remain a neutron star. Estimates vary, but it is widely believed that a dwarf with more than two or three times the Sun's mass will be so gravitationally overwhelmed that it must go on through the neutron star state in a few seconds on a course of total collapse.

Even the effective resistance of compacted neutrons cannot halt the gravitational intensity, which grows greater with every victory, that is, with every shrinkage of radius. The collapse time, as measured by clocks on the collapsing body, would be incredibly short. The collapse process, however, as it has appeared to observers on Earth or elsewhere—if they could see it at all—would seem to go on indefinitely, as mentioned before. The collapsing body generates gravitational fields so intense that the laws of Newton and of "classical" physics no longer apply. Time, space, distance are distorted out of all recognition.

The collapsing body reaches its Schwarzschild radius, and ceases to be accessible to observation from the outside. It has become a "black hole," a "singularity," a "has-been"—but is no longer a part of our observable universe. The process sets free vast quantities of energy, far vaster in fact, during the star's final accelerating stages, than during the earlier thermonuclear stages.

The cosmic catastrophe called a super-nova is an explosion arising from a great implosion or collapsing inward from dwarf size to neutron-star size. Total gravitational collapse is, so to speak, an utter and final implosion. But it is accompanied by an explosive release of energies and by a power, theoretically estimated, that alone can account for a number of astounding and sensational events observed by radio and optical astronomers during the past decade.

The theorists of gravitational collapse deal not only in measures of mass and energy and size (distance), but also in measured of relative densities. Here is a short table of comparative densities. Some are found in our everyday life on Earth. Others are associated with the processes believed to lead from the known dwarf stars to the supposed neutron stars and the confidently predicted cases of total collapse into "black holes".

TABLE 2

Approximate Densities
(in kilograms per cubic meter kg m^{-3})

Earth's atmosphere at sea level	1.2
Water	10^3
Sun (average)	1.4×10^3
Earth (average)	5.5×10^3
Lead, the metal	1.1×10^4
Core of the Sun	1.3×10^5
White dwarf star (average)	2×10^9
Nuclear substance in atoms	10^{17} to 10^{18}
A star of 10 times Sun's mass shrunken to its Schwarzschild radius of 3×10^4m	2×10^{17}
A star of Sun's mass shrunken to its Schwarzschild radius of 3×10^3m	2×10^{19}

The concluding case in the table is a wholly imaginary one, for some investigators estimate that a star with mass so "small" as that of our Sun will shrink only to the dwarf stage, and not on down to the ultimate Schwarzschild radius.

The quantity of compacted matter—the total mass, in other words—makes all the difference between the various careers and conclusions of the bodies we call by the name of "stars" during their period of long shining, before they approach their strange final phases.

7

And the Last Shall Be First....

We have moved toward a first understanding of the energetics of our enormous universe. We have seen that stars and galaxies shine through the ages, or swiftly explode and "implode" because of both gravitational *and* nuclear interactions.

The first roundup of scattered matter into sizeable stellar "lumps" takes place because of gravitation, and only when the assembled mass is sufficiently large and compacted do core temperatures rise high enough to kindle the first nuclear burning, which converts hydrogen into helium, plus energy.

From then until the star's nuclear fuel supply is used up and its interior is choked by iron "ash," nuclear interactions rather than gravitational ones supply most of the radiated energy.

This stage can go on for an enormous length of time. Our Sun, for example, is expected to reach its end only after a total of about ten billion years, during which it will have radiated out vast amounts of energy. Or is it, really, so large an amount of energy? Our ideas of size are all relative. We must constantly seek standards outside our own "common sense" and subjective impressions.

Such a standard we have at hand in the form of Einstein's equation $E = Mc^2$. The mass of our Sun, like the mass of every other body in the universe, provides a built-in energy yardstick. Each kilogram of mass, by that equation, is equivalent to c^2 joules—or 9×10^{16} J. (This "rest-mass" energy is in *addition* to any energy that may be added by motion, temperature, or chemical characteristics of the body.)

Using $E = Mc^2$ as a measure, we find that nuclear interactions can actually set free only a tiny fraction of the energy locked up in matter. Roughly, they can deliver no more than about one percent of the "rest-mass" energy. The other 99 percent of the energy remains untapped when a star reaches the end of its cycles of nuclear burning and begins to cool and shrink.

In the case of our Sun, for example, the equivalent of about 2×10^{28} kg will have poured through space as 1.8×10^{45} joule of electromagnetic energy—light, heat, radio, and x-rays. But what of the nearly 10^{47} joule of energy not yet unlocked from its cooling substance? A remarkable fact is now apparent: gravitation is the only known key to the unlocking of such additional energy. This seems especially noteworthy because it is often—and truly—said that gravitation is by far the weakest of all physical interactions or "forces," whereas nuclear interaction or "force" is enormously stronger.

Gravitation, however, is basically contradictory and in more than one way mysterious. It has characteristics which enable it, the least among the four known physical forces, to rise to first place, dominating the rest—*provided* sufficient gravitating mass is concentrated together into one single, dense body.

In order to reduce to its present size, the Sun yielded up about 3.8×10^{41} joule of energy. What would result from further shrinkage of the Sun's present radius to a radius roughly equal to that of the Earth—that is, from about 7×10^8 m to about 6.4×10^6 m? The gravitational binding energy of the Sun at that smaller radius would be somewhat more than 100 times the Sun's present binding energy. Hence such further shrinkage would provide about 3.8×10^{43} joule additional energy.

If still further contraction went on and the radius shrank to near the Schwarzschild size of only 3×10^3 m, a binding energy of *minus* 8.9×10^{46} J would be created.

We shall see later (Chapter 11) that it is not possible, in fact, for the shrinkage process to be halted at each and every point along the line. Once a star shrinks past the neutron star state, it is on a non-stop course to complete collapse, at an accelerating rate. The amount of its remaining energy released on the way will depend on such factors as its rotation, if it has any, and its departures from a fully spherical shape.

The collapse process, however, is estimated to release—in strikingly short times—up to about 9 percent of the mass-energy of nonrotating bodies; and up to more than 40 percent of the mass-energy of very rapidly rotating bodies. Since the long drawn out processes of nuclear burning during the "shining star" stage released no more than 1 to 2 percent of the mass-energy then available, one can see why gravitational collapse ranks as a far more effective and explosive energy extractor than even the nuclear processes. Yet gravitational collapse is founded on gravitation, feeblest among all the basic physical interactions measured by men thus far. Within this paradox may be found wealths of information and insight.

Since gravitation can unlock such great stores of energy, how can it be called the feeblest of all physical interactions thus far recognized?

(1) There are four such interactions or forces. Three of them were identified long after Newton had brought an amazing mathematical order to the observed behavior of bodies obeying gravitational interactions, the first of the four.

(2) The next to be recognized and interpreted was the electromagnetic interaction. It operates between charged particles, and also between charges travelling in wires (currents). Accelerated charges radiate power at many frequencies including light, radiant heat, x-rays, and radio waves.

Every complete atom is a balanced electrical system, with the positively charged protons in the nucleus retaining a like number of negatively charged electrons orbiting at great distances relative to the size of the tiny central nucleus.

Electrical interactions, like gravitational interactions, diminish according to the inverse square of the distance separating the interactive bodies. However, there is a great difference between these two kinds of interactions. Every bit of matter gravitationally attracts every other bit; but only objects with *unlike* electrical charge attract each other; those with like charges *repel* each other to a similar extent.

Two electrons, each with a minimal negative charge, repel each other; so, too, do two protons, each with a positive charge. However, a negative charge (such as an electron) attracts a positive charge (such as a proton), and vice versa. Thus, polarity plays a basic role in the electromagnetic interactions.

(3) Now, the nuclei of atoms contain various numbers of protons—from only one in the hydrogen nucleus to as many as 90 or more in radioactive elements. How can these mutually repelling positive protons be held together in so tiny a volume? An answer was found in the strange "strong" or nuclear force. This force operates powerfully, but only over very short distances, and dwindles to nothing far more rapidly than by an inverse square rule. At *extremely* short distances it reverses itself and becomes a repelling rather than an attracting force.

Within the limited range of its attraction, the strong interaction is about 100 times as potent as the electromagnetic interaction. Also, it operates with extreme rapidity. Among the scores of particles known to modern physicists, several important ones, including electrons, and muons (positive or negative), are never involved in strong interactions. On the other hand, uncharged particles, such as neutrons and pions are never involved in electromagnetic interactions.

(4) Latest to be identified are the "weak" interactions. They are about 10^{12} times weaker than the strong interactions; and about 10^{10} times weaker than the electromagnetic interactions. The "decay" of a neutron into a proton, an electron, and a neutrino is one common weak interaction. Neutrinos and anti-neutrinos are involved only in such weak interactions.

The more potent an interaction, the more rapid the changes

it brings about. Thus, a strong interaction change may be completed within 10^{-22} seconds (less than a billionth of a billionth of one second). A typical "transaction" of electromagnetic interaction may take place in 10^{-9} or 10^{-8} seconds, and a weak interaction transaction is as "long" as 10^{-6} seconds.

How do gravitational processes compare with those of the other three interactions? Gravitation's interactions are so extremely weak that gravitation seems, at first, almost too faint to merit consideration as a physical force. For example, the force of electrical repulsion between two electrons is about 5×10^{43} times as great as the gravitational attraction between the two electrons at the same distance. This amount of force is 50 times greater than a million multiplied by itself seven times! Such a discrepancy is almost too large to comprehend.

If we examine the "balance of forces" or interactions in a structure such as a typical atom, we find the disproportion almost as extreme. Like other bodies, an atom, in theory at least, may have energies associated with each of the four interactions. If we use the atom's strong (nuclear) energy as our unit, then we find that the other three energies have roughly this rapidly diminishing pattern: electromagnetic $= 10^{-2}$; weak $= 10^{-12}$; gravitational $= 10^{-40}$.

The proton, positively charged, has a mass nearly 2000 times that of the negative electron. The electrical repulsion of one proton for another is about 10^{36} times the gravitational attraction at the same distance. These are fantastically large discrepancies: gravitation showing itself from 10^{43} to 10^{36} times weaker than the electromagnetic interaction.

No wonder that gravitation plays practically no direct role in particle, nuclear, or atomic physics! We can understand also that the actual gravitational forces are extremely tiny even when these forces are between bodies on Earth that are quite massive in comparison to our human bodies.

Many a striking example of this fact has been given. Think of two massive diesel locomotives, weighing 400 tons each, standing side by side, with only 12 feet separating their center-lines. The gravitational attraction they have for each other is a tiny force—sometimes less than 2 ounces! If we compare the force of the locomotives' mutual attraction with the force (weight) that the Earth exerts on them, the latter is about 13 million times the former.

Two people of ordinary weight standing one meter apart exert on each other an attractive force of less than 1/25 milligram weight. Or, to leave the "weighty" conditions on earth and move to the weightless state, consider two "space-walking" astronauts floating freely just 1 meter apart, and making no use of jets to influence their relative motion. Their mutual gravitational attraction would "accelerate" them together so slowly that they would draw but 3 cm nearer in the first hour, 9 cm in the second, 15 cm in the third. About 5 hours would elapse before their mutual gravitational attraction had drawn them together.

No wonder that almost countless centuries, millenia, and even eons are required for the gravitational collection and compaction of sizable stellar objects from the scattered dust and atomic clouds of space!

Miracles of increasing masses—Gravitation, alone among the four interactions, has one striking characteristic that moves it from insignificance to equality, and finally to dominance as greater and greater mass accumulates. This process is like a most melodramatic race; gravitation, the tortoise of interactions, at first hopelessly outdistanced by the swift and potent hare of strong nuclear force, somehow pulls up even, and finally finishes first, accompanied by spectacular cosmic effects.

This happens because of the "all for one, one for all" operation of the gravitational interaction. Each particle in an aggregate attracts each other particle, no matter what distances separate them, and without regard to polarity, negative or positive. Gravitational energies are intensified, as we have seen, in proportion to the square of the total masses of the aggregated bodies, and inversely as the radius of the volume in which that mass has been concentrated.

$$E_{grav} = - \frac{GM^2}{R}$$

Let us illustrate, by a series of examples of bodies of increasing mass, how the energy of gravitational interaction begins far behind; then, growing swiftly, overtakes first the energy of electromagnetic interaction, and finally the energy of the strong, or nuclear, interaction itself. In this comparison we can disregard the energy of the weak interaction (Table 3).

Ten cases are singled out. They begin with the 1 gram of mass of a droplet of water (a) and rise to the mass of our Sun itself (e). Then, holding fast to this mass, we show step by step, (f) through (j), how successive shrinkages in size increase average density, and raise the gravitational energy until it dominates all other energy sources in the body.

These figures are approximate only. For the last four examples, (g) through (j), they are based on projections and assumptions from conditions typical of smaller, less compacted masses. The density is given in terms of an average, as if the body were uniformly dense all the way through. We know, of course, that the core densities and pressures are vastly greater than those near the surface in the Sun; and they would show the same general pattern also in a dwarf star, and in the structures still more shrunken than the dwarf star.

The asterisk beside the average density for the neutron star calls attention to the fact that the density of nuclear matter itself—the proton-neutron structures forming atomic nuclei—lies in just this range: 10^{17} to 10^{18} kg/m^3—or 10^{16} to 10^{17} times the density of water.

The final extreme case, that of the so-called "Schwarzschild radius" star, indicates average density about 1000 times as great.

TABLE 3

Body	Mass (in kg)	Average Density (in kg/m^3)	*Energy Ratios* Gravitational to Electro-Magnetic Energies	Gravitational to Strong (Nuclear) Energies
(a) Drop of water, (one gram)	10^{-3}	10^3	10^{-24}	10^{-26}
(b) Sphere of iron (radius 1 meter)	3×10^4	7.6×10^3	10^{-19}	10^{-21}
(c) Earth	6×10^{24}	5.5×10^3	10^{-7}	10^{-9}
(d) Jupiter	2×10^{27}	1.3×10^3	10^{-3}	10^{-5}
(e) Sun	2×10^{30}	1.4×10^3	10^{-2}	10^{-4}
(f) Dwarf star (mass of Sun, radius like Earth)	2×10^{30}	2 b 10^9	Equal	10^{-2}
(g) Smaller dwarf star (same mass, radius 1/10 of Earth)	2×10^{30}	2×10^{12}	10	10^{-1}
(h) Still more shrunken star (same mass, radius 1/100 of Earth)	2×10^{30}	2×10^{15}	10^2	Equal
(i) Neutron star (same mass, radius 1/400 of Earth)	2×10^{30}	$1.4\times10^{17*}$	4×10^2	4
(j) "Schwarzschild radius" star (same mass, radius 1/4000 of Earth)	2×10^{30}	1.4×10^{20}	4 to 5$\times$10	40 to 50

It suggests that, according to the bold assumptions behind this table, matter can somehow be compressed to densities even greater than those of nuclear particles.

One important addition needs to be made to the ideas illustrated by the table. It may suggest that gravitational energies can overtake electromagnetic and nuclear energies only in bodies that have become super-dense—bodies compacted to an extent never found on Earth, or in its innermost interior where pressures rise so much higher than at the surface. The fact is, however, that conglomerations of matter *with sufficient total mass* can produce the primacy of gravitational over electromagnetic and nuclear energies, even though the average densities of the collection, and even its interior density, remain rather low by Earth standards.

For example, if we could fashion a sphere with about 1000 times the Earth's radius, then even though its average density were no greater than that of the Earth (5.5×10^3 kg/m³), that Super-earth would contain gravitational energy as great as its nuclear energy.

Or if we could fashion a Super-sun with 10 times the radius of our own Sun, then even though its average density were no greater than that of the Sun (about 1.4×10^3 kg/m³), it too would contain as much gravitational energy as nuclear energy. A body with average density no greater than that of water on Earth will have gravitational energy equal to nuclear energy, *provided* its radius is about a dozen times that of our Sun.

Even more striking is the concept we find when we consider a dust cloud whose total mass is about that of an entire galaxy; that is, equal to the mass of 10^{11} Suns, or about 2×10^{41} kg. Such a cloud would contain as much gravitational as nuclear energy, and be at the very point of gravitational collapse, while its average density was only 0.41 kg/m³—or *less than* the density of air at Earth's surface.

Let us repeat an important fact: The simplest form of equation by which the gravitational energy of a single body, or conglomeration of matter, can be estimated is, as we have seen, $E_{grav} = GM^2/R$. This means that, if total dimensions remain unchanged, gravitational energy must increase as the *square* of increasing mass. Nuclear and electrical energies, however, will increase merely as the mass itself. It is a case of the second power growth inevitably overtaking and passing the first power growth.

But what if a mass remains constant while its size shrinks? As a sphere shrinks to one half its former radius, its total gravitational energy doubles—goes up just two times, even though its average *density* has meantime increased eightfold.

Sheer amount of mass is, after all, more important in these cosmic contests between gravitation and nuclear energies than is mere shrinkage and densification, though those also play their part.

Objects of the size we can make or manipulate on Earth are far too deficient in total mass to provide men with extractable energy by means of gravitational collapse. Perhaps this is a good thing, in view of the fatalities and fears that have already resulted from the conquest of nuclear (strong) interactions for military uses. If gravitational bombs could be stockpiled, in addition to the overkill stores of *nuclear* bombs, our troubled world would certainly be even worse off.

Only within bodies approaching or surpassing the mass of our own Sun does the gravitational tortoise overtake and leave behind the swift hares of nuclear and electromagnetic energies. Only there can gravitational forces "crush" atoms and squeeze smaller even the ultimate nuclear substances that remain.

The changes in the relative strengths of these great physical interactions provide a spectacle of strange drama, in which, in truth, the last finally finishes first. Such events calls to mind the oriental tales of the sealed vial that proved to contain a genii, a tiny nothing, hardly a voice. But unstoppered, released, allowed to grow, the genii becomes great enough to cover the sky, to darken the Sun, and to swallow up the very stars!

8

Does Gravity, Too, Have Radiation?

In 1916, amidst the First World War, which he detested and deplored, Albert Einstein revealed his general theory of relativity. It was an enormous extension of Newton's analysis of gravitation, as well as of Einstein's earlier "special" theory of relativity.

Einstein's new, more inclusive and subtle equations of general relativity proved to be equivalent to those of Newton for situations involving only weak gravitational fields and velocities that were very small compared with that of light, c. But where gravitation became intense or velocities approached c, general relativity showed results differing significantly from those of all previous analyses.

General relativity and its mathematics lie far beyond the scope of this book. However, it is important to know that Einstein's historic equation for gravitation contains a quantity symbolized by ϕ_{ab}, which specialists call "the tensor gravitational potential." When applied to masses at rest relative to each other, this potential behaves like the Newtonian gravitational potential ϕ, previously mentioned.

In other relationships, such as when masses are in motion relative to each other, a close and complete analogy exists between the laws these masses obey and the laws obeyed by electrical charges in comparable situations.

We can, in fact, say that Einstein's general relativity provides for gravitational fields the same kind of mathematics that scientists have long provided for electrical fields. Newton's law for gravitational force between two attracting masses parallels closely Coulomb's law for electrical force between two attracting (or repelling) charges. Pictorially, we can see the close likeness between the electrical and gravitational situations. In Figure 8-1 we see a spherical electrified body Q surrounded by the imaginary lines of electrical force directed outward in straight lines leading from the body's geometrical center. The dashed circles suggest the lines of equal electrical potential, symmetrical around the source of this "static" electrification.

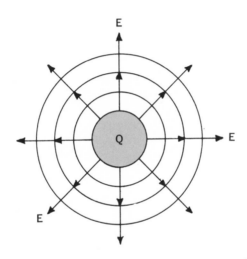

Figure 8-1. The electrical field around a static charge Q (at center) may be pictured this way. The electrical force lines are arrowed outward. Hence if two like charges (negative-negative or positive-positive) interact, their force lines "collide," and they repel each other. Two unlike charges (negative-positive), however, attract each other.

In Figure 8-2, we make a similar representation of the lines of gravitational force and the zones of gravitational potential around a spherical mass M. We see the same surrounding pattern.

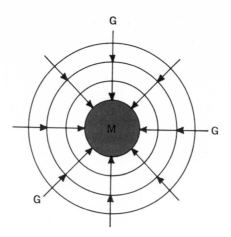

Figure 8-2. The gravitational field around a static mass M (at center) resembles the electrical field. Here the lines of force are arrowed inward. Masses always attract each other gravitationally. There is no repulsive action, as there is between like charges in the electrical case.

In both the gravitational and electrical cases, the mutual forces exerted by the masses (M_1 and M_2) and by the charges (Q_1 and Q_2) diminish as $1/D^2$, where D is the distance from the center of one mass or charge to that of the other mass or charge.

What if the charges are in motion relative to one another? If we observe and measure a charge Q while it moves relative to us, or we to it, then we see something that was not there when we observed it as a stationary charge. Motion has created a *magnetic* field in conjunction with the charge's electrical field (Figure 8-3).

Something quite analogous happens also when masses are in uniform motion relative to us, or when we are moving uniformly relative to them. New and different gravitational fields are created, the gravitational equivalents of the magnetic fields. Dr. Robert L. Forward of Hughes Research Laboratory, Malibu, has suggested for them the name "protational" fields (Figure 8-4).

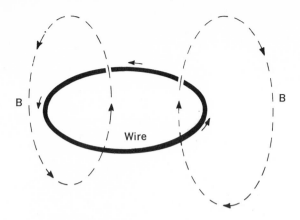

Figure 8-3. Here electric charges are moving uniformly around a wire—in other words, a current is flowing in the wire. The result of charge in motion is the creation of a *magnetic* field in addition to the *electircal* field. The direction of the magnetic field lines, looping around the wire, is indicated by the three dashed circles labelled B. This is the basis for the operation of "electromagnets" and solenoid coils.

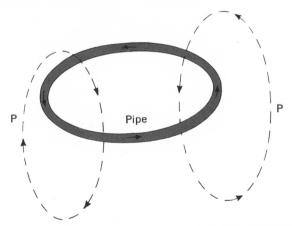

Figure 8-4. Mass in motion also creates a new kind of field, analagous (though far weaker) to the magnetic fields formed around moving charges. Here a liquid mass is circulated in a pipe, as shown by arrows. The magnetic-like field lines are indicated by the two dashed circles labelled P.

In order to keep the diagram as simple as possible the figure does not show another field analagous to the electrical field of a charge (current) flowing in a circular wire. That other field would lie in the same plane as the circular pipe and it circular lines of force would be concentric with the pipe. The directions of those lines, however, would be opposite to the direction in which the liquid flows inside the pipe. Gravitational fields are full of surprises.

Dr. Forward stresses that what one can do with electrons and magnetic fields can also be done with masses and "protational" fields. Such fields have fascinating characteristics. The purposes of this book require us, however, to concentrate on the third case—that of the *accelerated,* rather than the uniform, motion of charges and of masses.

If the electric charge Q is accelerated, either in a straight line or in a curved course, it *radiates.* It launches energy into space in patterns of waves related to the frequency of its motion. This is very much part of our everyday world, for radio and TV depend wholly on the radiations emitted by myriads of accelerated charges (electrons) surging back and forth in transmitting antennas.

With radiation, and radiation alone, we have the situation in which portions of energy are, at times, with neither the transmitting nor the receiving devices; they are, rather, en route from one to the other. In fact, the radiation journeys may be very long. Astronomers make their photographs with light that has been under way for hundreds, thousands, millions of years.

The force that radiation exerts has travelled as a wave obeying a mathematical wave equation. Just such an equation or element is contained also in Einstein's elegant and difficult gravitation "recipe" for general relativity. And because the same mathematical situation holds for the electrical and the gravitational case, we find that accelerated masses should also launch their own radiations—*gravitational waves.*

That was Einstein's own conclusion, published in 1917. The new intensification of studies on relativistic gravitation has brought a great upwelling of interest in gravitational waves, despite the many difficulties that exist in detecting or dealing with these waves.

How radiation overwhelms the static effects—Forces exerted by static charges (electrical) or masses (gravitational) diminish as the inverse square of the distance over which they act—as $1/D^2$. But this is not so with radiation. Forces exerted by radiation fall off only as the inverse first power—that is, as $1/D$.

A simple basic equation covers the case of the forces exerted by radiation from an accelerated charge Q_1. If the charge is accelerated at the rate A, and the test or responding body has a charge of Q_2, then the force on Q_2 will be:

$$F_{rad} = \frac{KQ_1Q_2A}{Dc^2}$$

Here K is a "constant of proportionality," and c is the velocity of light. This tells us that if we double the acceleration, leaving all else unchanged, the exerted force doubles also.

The same pattern also applies precisely to two masses, M_1 and M_2, when the former is given an acceleration A, and the latter is used to measure the resulting force:

$$F_{rad} = \frac{GM_1M_2A}{Dc^2}$$

It need be no surprise to find the familiar gravitational constant G as the constant of proportionality here also. (One small note of caution: for simplicity, we have assumed that the acceleration of Q_1 is at right angles to a line connecting it with Q_2; and similarly that the acceleration of M_1 is at right angles to a line connecting it to M_2.)

Radiative forces, however weak, must finally equal and then

outstrip static force effects, as one moves further and further from the accelerated mass which is the source of both kinds of forces. Suppose, for example, we find at a distance of 1 length unit from an accelerated body that that body's static gravitation force is a million (10^6) times stronger than its radiative force effect. If, then, we make a new test at a distance of 2×10^6 length units, the static force is diminished to $1/(4 \times 10^{12})$ of what it was while the radiative force effect is diminished only to $1/(2 \times 10^6)$. The latter will now, at this distance, be twice as large as the former.

Each further increase in distance intensifies this swamping of the static by the radiative forces. The static or common gravitation is often referred to as the "near" effect while the radiation is called the "far" effect. Radiation takes precedence over static forces as we go out to greater distances, whether we are working electrically or gravitationally.

During the half-century following the first publication of Einstein's general relativity equations, little work was done on the gravitational waves implied there. It was indeed quite clear that these waves must be very weak compared with electromagnetic waves. That was assured, in part, by the very small size of the gravitational constant G (6.67×10^{-11} m^3 kg^{-1} s^{-2}).

Quantitative recipes or equations were developed, however, showing the power in watts that should be radiated by known masses accelerated at various rates, including the acceleration of rotational motion (like that of the Moon around Earth, identified with acceleration by Newton himself).

There are also such equations for the power radiated by an accelerated electrical charge, but we shall move at once to the gravitational case. What would be the simplest form of a transmitter of gravitational waves? We find we cannot suggest *just one* mass shaken back and forth. For every action there is an equal and opposite reaction, Newton said; and we are also reminded of a rule known as the conservation of momentum.

Hence we must deal with two masses accelerated relative to each other. Here (Figure 8-5) we have two masses connected by a spring, at the ends of which they oscillate (accelerate) back and forth, extending out as in A, coming together as in B, then out again as in C. These masses on the spring could be an antenna to radiate gravitational waves. Or, if they are allowed to respond passively, they could form an antenna for receiving the waves.

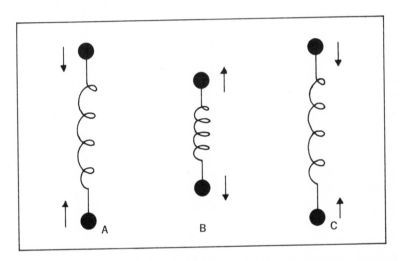

Figure 8-5. A simple gravitational antenna. Two masses are connected by a spring. They move alternately toward, and away from, each other. If their oscillation is caused by mechanical force, then they radiate gravitationally, according to general relativity theory. If they are merely passive "responders" or receivers, then they are made to oscillate by arriving gravitational waves, according to the same theory.

For our purposes here, however, a simple model transmitter of gravitational waves could be two equal masses spun rapidly at the ends of a connecting bar, D being the distance between their mass-centers (Figure 8-6). If M is the mass of each, then we find that the power radiated through gravitational waves will be proportional to the product of the masses (M^2), to the fourth

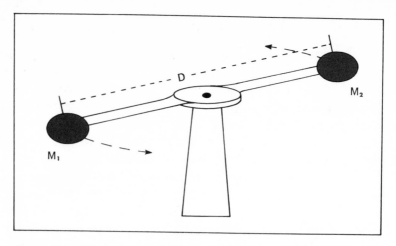

Figure 8-6. Masses (M_1 and M_2) spun rapidly also radiate gravitational waves, but the radiated power remains tiny unless *very* large masses are spun *very* fast. Hence scientists look to fast-spinning binary stars in the sky, rather than to laboratory generators of gravitational waves on Earth for detectable evidence of such radiations.

power of the distance between them (D^4), and to the *sixth* power of the angular velocity w with which they are spun (w^6):

$$P_{rad} = kM^2D^4w^6$$

Here k stands for a constant of proportionality.

Instead of the angular velocity, we can use the time, or period T, for one full rotation. Then the equation takes this form:

$$P_{rad} = \frac{BM^2D^4}{T^6}$$

Here B is another constant of proportionality. In fact, it contains, among other things, G in its numerator and c^5 in its denominator. When figured out, B proves to have an extremely small numerical value:

$$B = 3.75 \times 10^{-51} \text{ m}^{-2} \text{ kg}^{-1} \text{ s}^3$$

The result, we find, is that radiated gravitational waves are extremely *un*powerful unless very large masses are spun extremely fast. In fact, to generate detectable gravitational waves by a laboratory machine we should have to spin masses far beyond the rupture or bursting points of the strongest materials known on earth.

Are there no "natural" sources of gravitational waves free from such limitations? There are, in our Solar system, in our great Galaxy, and indeed in the myriads of galaxies scattered throughout visible space. Every planet is a mass swinging around the Sun, which also, in turn, swings—to a far lesser but yet undeniable extent—around that planet.

When we calculate the gravitational radiations emitted by the combinations of various planets and the Sun, we find extremely small powers. In the case of the Earth the gravitational radiation comes to less than 1 watt, barely the power consumed by a small flashlight bulb. Even Jupiter, giant in our system, radiates in its orbital motion less than 35 watts, the power consumed by small incandescent light.

There are, however, "natural" radiators of quite different character, with masses of sunlike size spinning around each other in tight circles, completed in a tiny fraction of the time that even the planet Mercury takes to move through its orbit.

A great many of the stars we see are not single. They are pairs, binaries, orbiting each other. It has been estimated that in our Galaxy alone—within some 300 light-years of our Earth—there must be about 100,000 such binary systems *with periods of less then 24 hours.*

A much simplified equation permits us to compute the power of gravitational radiation from a binary system, both of whose stars have equal mass M with an inter-center separation of D:

$$P_{rad} = K \left(\frac{M}{D} \right)^5$$

Here K is another constant of proportionality, equal in this case to very nearly 13 G^4/c^5.

The complete equation, with the constant part placed first and the variable part last can be expressed approximately this way:

$$P_{rad} = \frac{13G^4}{c^5} \times \left(\frac{M}{D}\right)^5$$

With such a "recipe" it is possible to compute what would be the gravitational radiation from a binary system, each of whose stars was a white dwarf, with mass like that of the Sun $(2 \times 10^{30}$ kg), and each of which revolved around the other with a separation of less than 8 times the radius of our Earth—that is to say, with an inter-center distance D of 5×10^7 m.

The result proves to be an enormous radiated power—about 10^{31} watts. This is about 25,000 times the power radiated constantly by the Sun itself. Such a gigantic output of power in the form of gravitational radiation is possible only because of the extremely compacted and shrunken states of the dwarf stars forming the binary system. These stars are revolving at a distance D which is about one-thirtieth the diameter of our Sun; and each of the pair has a mass equal to the Sun's though it has been collapsed to a size like that of our Earth.

The resulting huge outpouring of gravitational radiation rapidly carries off the kinetic (motion) energy of the binary system. The orbit of the system "decays"—meaning that both dwarfs spiral in toward each other. The distance D diminishes. The equation tells us that as D dwindles the radiated power rises rapidly. In fact, since the relationship is $(1/D)^5$, reducing D to half means increasing radiated power 2^5 or 32 times!

This is an accelerating process. By the time the radiated power rises to 10^{38} watts the binary system has less than a fraction of a year left before the stars come together. When power climbs to 10^{42} watts, less than two minutes remain. At

10^{45} W, less than 1 s is left before the end, which comes as the radiation rises to a peak of about 10^{47} W. The two stars, having spun together, probably form a single irregular body, spinning yet faster than the system from which this new body was formed.

Theory makes clear that a single spinning body emits gravitational radiation only if its shape is somewhat lopsided or unsymmetrical around its axis of rotation. A perfect sphere could spin at any rate without radiating. But every lump, hump, or bump on its surface would radiate—and at a rate proportional to the *6th power* of the rotational rate.

Pulsar possibilities—Do collapsed binary systems typically give birth to pulsars? Pulsars are the strange objects emitting complex radio "beeps" at rapid and regular intervals. Unknown until the late 1960s, they had been located to the number of more than 40 by early 1970.

Accurately measured periods of pulsing show only two pulsars with intervals longer than 2 seconds. The great majority pulse at intervals between 1 1/2 and 1/3 seconds. Most rapid beeper of them all is the famous pulsar centered in the Crab nebula, product of an ancient super-nova explosion. Its signal comes in about 30 times per second, its period being close to 0.0333 s.

The pulsars are powerful radio emitters, scattered around our own Galaxy. Their precisely spaced signals show they must be bodies revolving at fantastic rates, their radio beams sweeping our earth each revolution.

Imagine massive stars spinning between 40 and 2000 rpm! Only if shrunken to ultradensities and tiny dimensions could they spin so swiftly without being torn to bits. Hence authorities are almost unanimous in ascribing to them radii as small as 25 or 30 km, with perhaps much greater mass than our Sun.

Two typical pulsar characteristics are especially puzzling: (1) the period between beeps is extremely uniform, permitting measurements of time as precise as this 12-place decimal, giving the period in seconds for the pulsar named CP 0950: 0.253 065 032 86; and (2) a tiny lengthening of the period in commonly found over a long interval of time.

In other words, a pulsar is like a gigantic flywheel, spinning swiftly, steadily, but slowing down ever so little. Such pulsar deceleration is typically less than 1 part in 1 million million per period. It shows that the intense radio radiations are slowly draining off some of the neutron-star's vast spin-energy.

This drain, if continued, would in some cases suffice to spell finish to the pulsar within a few thousand years; and in other cases not until many millions of years had passed. Even odder is the fact that the records of some pulsars show periodic jumps or brief jagged reversals in the steady slowing process. A brief speed-up occurs, soon followed by resumption of the steady, slow decline. Hypotheses of internal "quakes" or slippages of substance within the neutron star itself have been advanced by way of explanation.

Pulsars embody staggering power. The mechanical energy of rotation of a swiftly spinning neutron pulsar is probably about 10^{42} joule. That energy is converted into powerful radio waves at the rate of about 10^{31} watts, or more than 20,000 times the power our sun emits in the form of light.

Only one pulsar has so far been seen by telescope—that in the Crab. The rest apparently emit too little light. They are known only by their unprecedented patterns of radio signals which were, for a time, suspected to be signals from "little green men" somewhere in distant space.

Spinning pulsars and orbiting binaries have much in common. Both reveal how vast rotational energies can be converted into radiations—electromagnetic and gravitational—and scattered widely in space. Both processes of energy conversion depends largely on drastic shrinkages in sizes and distances, accompanied by corresponding increases in densities of the stellar bodies involved.

Binaries and pulsars, especially the fast ones, have limited lifetimes. The more rapidly they spin, the shorter their life expectancies. Both kinds of spinning systems add to the spectacles of "incredible grandeur" indicated by the title of this book. But they are by no means the only mechanisms that may emit major amounts of radiation—gravitationally or in the form of radio waves. This may be accomplished by almost any swiftly accelerated transport of large amounts of material in space. That would include ejection of large amounts of gas, star substance, and plasma in the explosion of a super-nova.

Other explosive processes, as yet vaguely understood, are believed to occur in the cores, or inmost hearts, of many galaxies—perhaps repeatedly, at long intervals. The more turbulent and irregular such swift ejections of matter, the more pronounced should be their resulting gravitational radiations.

Another likely source of such radiation would be the rapid fall of a star, or even of an object of planetary dimensions, into an intensely gravitating neutron star; or perhaps into the ultimate "black hole" of a star that has undergone complete gravitational collapse. On the way down, in a matter of mere moments, such a falling body could spiral and gravitationally radiate energies equivalent to a large part of its total mass.

New evidence accumulates, new theories proliferate, and one may feel moved to exclaim, as did Horatio after the visitation of the ghost of the murdered king: "O day and night, but this is wondrous strange!"

Astronomers, physicists, and relativists could then well reply, using the same play on words that Shakespeare put into the mouth of Prince Hamlet:

> And therefore as a stranger give it welcome.
> There are more things in heaven and earth, Horatio,
> Than are dreamt of in your philosophy.

Strange patterns of gravitational waves—Gravitational waves must travel through space at c, the same velocity as that of electromagnetic waves. However, in other respects gravitational waves behave quite differently from electromagnetic waves.

First, let us look at the matter of *frequency*. If the charges (currents) in a radio transmitter oscillate with a frequency of 1 megahertz (10^6 times per second), that, too, will be the frequency of the resulting electromagnetic waves received at any distance. However, if a binary star system is revolving at the rate of once every 60 seconds, its gravitational waves will be received at just double that frequency—that is, at one full wave every 30 seconds. The reason for this is rather simple. Let us look at a binary system (Figure 8-7). At this instant we see both stars, A and B, as well as the suggestion of a gravitational wave such as might be perceived by a suitable receiver at R. Just *half* a full period later, B will be where A is now, and A where B is now. That situation will duplicate the one shown in the figure. Hence the physical pattern is repeated every half-period, and the resulting wave reflects this fact.

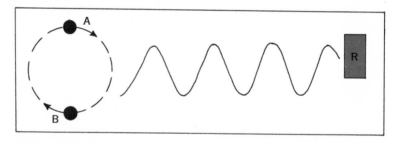

Figure 8-7. Why gravitational waves have *twice* the frequency of the rotation of the binary star systems in which they originate. A simplified view of such a system, seen looking "down" along the line of the axis around which both stars (A and B) revolve. The receiver—supposedly on Earth—is symbolized by R.

Such doubling of the rotational rate of the "transmitter" is typical of gravitational wave emission. But there are other and even more striking differences in the behavior of gravitational waves as compared with that of electromagnetic waves.

Figure 8-8 shows at left an accelerated charge—the "emitter"—

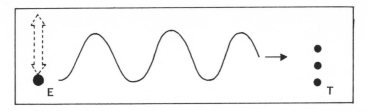

Figure 8-8. At left an oscillating charge (E) is emitting electromagnetic waves which travel toward the right where they act upon a group of test charges labelled T. The next figure (8-9) shows us how those charges will move under the influence of these waves.

and suggests the electromagnetic wave (resulting from the accelerated back-and-forth oscillation of such a charge) that would travel to a group of charged "test" particles at the right— such as electrons in a receiving antenna. As the wave passes these test particles, they are all shifted *together* up and down. Charges disposed in a circle before the wave arrives would be shifted, still in a circle, first one way, then the other (Figure 8-9).

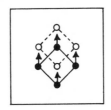

Figure 8-9. Here we are looking at a group of test charges arranged in a square (black circles), as seen from the direction in which the wave originated in Fig 8-8. As the waves pass, these charges move up and down (oscillate) together. Each moves a like amount, to the location indicated by the open circles above; and then back again (black circles). This is quite different from the movement of test masses when affected by the arrival of gravitational waves.

Quite different is the effect of the arrival of a *gravitational* wave. In Figure 8-10 we are looking in the direction of O, from which a gravitational wave is coming toward us. A group of 8 masses placed in a circle provides our reveiver or detector. Now the wave arrives, and its first half-cycle shifts our test masses into a pattern like that in Figure 8-11. The masses at top and bottom have been moved away from each other; those at the two sides have been moved toward each other. The former circle pattern has become an oblong or ellipse.

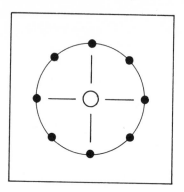

Figure 8-10. A group of test masses disposed in a circle, before the arrival of gravitational radiation (waves) which are coming from a distant source at O, in the direction toward which we are looking.

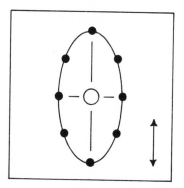

Figure 8-11. The same test masses as the peak of the first half-wave passes. The masses at top and bottom have been moved *away* from each other; those at right and left *toward* each other. The masses are now disposed in an oblong or ellipse.

By the end of the first half-cycle, the masses shift back to their circular arrangement, as in 8-10, but continue on until they look like 8-12. Now the top and bottom masses have been moved toward each other, and the masses at the two sides have been moved away from each other. Again we have an oblong, or ellipse, as if we had rotated by 90 degrees the pattern of 8-11. Finally, when the end of the full wave arrives, the test masses will be in their original circular arrangement, as in 8-10.

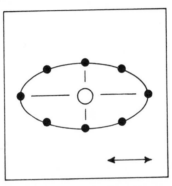

Figure 8-12. The same test masses as the "peak" of the second half wave passes. Now top and bottom masses have been moved *toward* each other, so that they are closer than they were in 8-10; and those at right and left *away* from each other, so that they are farther apart than they were in 8-10, and so, on and on, as long as the gravitational radiation impinges on the masses.

Thus gravitational waves always produce a perpendicularly polarized motion, or shearing effect, which is almost unknown in the action of electromagnetic waves on test charges.

Now let us visualize complete gravitational radiation in terms of the displacements it will produce in masses that it meets as it moves. Figure 8-13 shows as source, at left, a binary star system revolving around a midpoint in a repeating orbit, marked by V. Two types of radiation emanate from this radiating source.

At the upper left we see radiation moving off along the axis of rotation, perpendicular to the plane in which the two stars

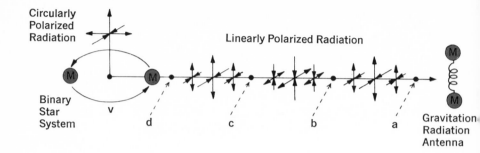

Figure 8-13. Gravitational radiation from a binary star system, indicated at left by (M) and (M). Two types of polarization or motion patterns are radiated, depending on the direction in which the stars are orbiting with respect to the plane. At right angles to that plane, along the axis of rotation (either "up" or "down") the emitted radiation is "circularly polarized," as shown at left.

At any direction lying in the plane, however, the radiation is "linearly polarized," and the resulting motions imposed on the masses encountered by the moving waves are indicated by the arrows, alternately showing motion *toward,* and *away from,* the direction of propagation. That propagation is at the cosmic speed limit, *c,* the same as the velocity of light in empty space.

No other form of wave motion, whether light, radio, sound, or surface waves on liquid, has the motion patterns quite like these of gravitational radiation which were envisaged by Einstein's general relativity theory.

are revolving. This radiation is "circularly polarized." If we were looking down along the axis of rotation toward the binary stars, the two sets of arrows (one pointing outward away from the axis, the other inward toward the axis) would seem to be rotating around that axis. Light, too, can be "circularly polarized," but in a manner quite different from this gravitational radiation.

Toward the right, moving in the plane of the orbital pattern, we see one "ray" of "linearly polarized radiation." It includes 1½ full waves or cycles: the sector a-b-c is one full wave; and c-d is a half wave. The arrows show the motions that will be imparted to masses encountered by each part of the wave as it arrives.

Let us consider just the two masses, top and bottom, in the "gravitational radiation antenna" or receiver at right. As the wave sector a-b passes, they will be moved apart, returning to "normal" position when b arrives. Then as the sector b-c passes, they will be moved together, once again returning to "normal" when c arrives. With the arrival of sector c-d, the spreading apart is repeated; and so, on and on, for as long as the gravitational waves stream past.

If we mounted a second antenna, or detecting unit, crossways (at right angles to the one shown at right), then at any instant its masses would be moving in a manner *opposite* to the masses of the first antenna, pictured in the diagram as lying vertically.

The other antenna, accordingly, would be mounted horizontally, and very near to the vertical one. Then, when the masses of the vertical antenna would be approaching each other, those of the horizontal antenna would be moving away from each other; and vice versa. Such polarization, or contradictory motion depending on orientation in space, is typical of these strange gravitational radiations, as called for by general relativity theory.

Gravitational radiations are travelling, wavelike alterations in space-time relationships. They are not vector waves, like electromagnetic radiations such as light and radio. They are not scalar waves. They are so-called *tensor* waves. As such, they exhibit characteristics all their own. Their unique qualities make them difficult to detect and measure, but also make them fascinating to study and to try to fit into the general patterns of the physical universe, whose unsolved problems must constantly change, but never be exhausted.

9

Sitting Cylinders and Strange Signals

General Relativity and Gravitational Waves, a small and difficult book, by Joseph Weber, professor of physics, University of Maryland, appeared in 1961. About a quarter of its 200 pages were devoted mainly to "treatment of the theoretical and experimental aspects of gravitational radiation."

Weber's preface mentioned the recently renewed interest in Einstein's general relativity theories, and noted that "technological advances of the past two decades make possible some new gravitation experiments and more precise ways of doing the older ones."

By the time his book appeared, Weber, with various students and associates, had been working several years on the design of the first laboratory experiments seeking to detect gravitational waves. The resulting "gravitational radiation detectors" combine elements of utmost simplicity and ultrasophisticated modern instrumentation.

As suggested by Figure 9-1, each detector is basically a massive metal "chunk," in cylindrical shape, serving as a "receiving antenna" for the expected gravitational waves. The cylinder, with a mass of about 1½ tons, is suspended at its center by a single cable, and its ends are free to move in the vacuum chamber that serves as its enclosure.

Around the middle of the cylinder are mounted rows of extremely sensitive strain gauges, transducers which convert minute motions of the metal into electric voltages. They work

Figure 9-1. Dr. Joseph Weber, professor of physics at the University of Maryland, works on the enormous aluminum cylinder that makes up the "antenna" of one of his gravitational radiation detectors. The vacuum cover has been removed. Arranged in five rows around the middle of the cylinder are the sensitive strain detectors which convert tiny stress-induced changes of shape into electrical signals.

The mounting that supports the metal mass is buffered and elastic, to damp out possible mechanical disturbances from the foundations and the earth beneath.

on the same principle as sensitive cartridge "pick-ups" used in record players.

The currents from these strain gauges, when suitably detected and amplified, are converted into "wiggles" on long moving rolls of graph paper from which it is easy to read the exact time at which any particular "high point" of the trace appears.

Figure 9-2 gives a schematic sequence. At left rests the massive cylinder, its mounting equipped with rubber pads to eliminate mechanical motions from outside. The electrical output of the transducers goes to electronic apparatus cooled with liquid helium to reduce disturbance caused by thermal motions of atoms and electrons in the circuitry. (See the Dewar flask arrangement.) The output from here is further amplified and then actuates the "pens" which trace the resulting "wiggles."

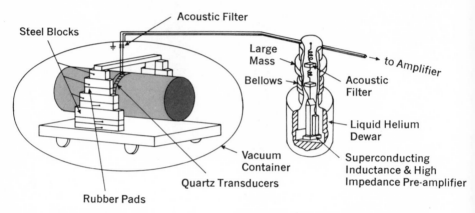

Dr. Joseph Weber, University of Maryland

Figure 9-2. This schematic drawing shows essentials of the gravitational radiation detectors used by Joseph Weber in his pioneering efforts. At left is the "antenna," an aluminum cylinder some 2 feet in diameter and 5 feet long, weighing 1½ tons. A gravitational wave passing through it creates a shape distortion which is detected by the array of "transducers" belted around the cylinder's middle. Their electrical output is modified by sophisticated electronic devices, amplified, and then recorded on a graph. Helium is used to cool the electronic apparatus in order to reduce the "noise," or disturbance caused by thermal motions of atoms and electrons.

Figure 9-3 shows Dr. Weber pointing to one significant record—an especially large jump in output recorded by his detector at the University of Maryland at the same moment as an especially large jump recorded by another detector, placed about 1000 km distant, at the Argonne Laboratory, Chicago, Illinois. Such a "coincidence" between significant jumps on the two widely separated detectors is shown in Figure 9-4. The

Figure 9-3. The coincidences that count . . . Dr. Joseph Weber, pioneer in the search for evidence of gravitational radiations, points out a pair of coincident responses by detectors placed a thousand kilometers apart. The trace at top comes from the readings of the detector at the University of Maryland; that below from a similar detector at the Argonne Laboratory, Chicago, Ill.

electrical output of the Argonne detector was transmitted by telephone lines to Maryland, where the two separate records were recorded and later analyzed in search of just such coincidences.

The trace on the graph for each detector constantly "wiggled" with small variations attributable to thermal motions of the detector cylinders and the electrical circuitry. Only when exceptionally large jumps were recorded at corresponding times on both detectors could a significant "coincidence" be established.

By mid-June of 1969 the journal *Physical Review Letters* published a report from Weber under the challenging title "Evidence for Discovery of Gravitational Radiation." It summarized observations indicating that the number of observed

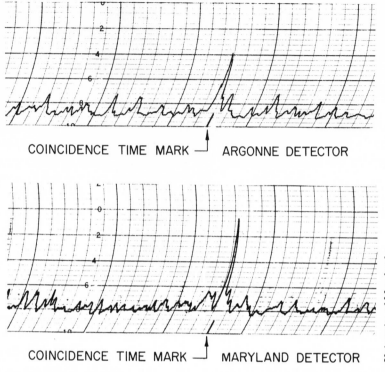

COINCIDENCE TIME MARK ⌐ ARGONNE DETECTOR

COINCIDENCE TIME MARK ⌐ MARYLAND DETECTOR

University of Maryland

Figure 9-4. A close-up look at a case of coincidence in readings from two widely separated detectors seeking gravitational radiation. The top trace shows the time mark of the extra high "hump" recorded by telephone lines from the detector at Chicago; the trace below the corresponding time mark for the even more distinctly marked "hump" in the trace from the detector at Maryland. Discovery of more "coincidences" than chance alone would be likely to produce, is what constitutes, at this time, the basis of evidence that gravitational radiation has been detected.

coincidences had been greater than could be accounted for by mere chance alone. Subsequently, additional data reenforced the earlier findings. By late February of 1970 a research summary by G. L. Wick in *Science* magazine was titled "Gravitational Waves: The Evidence Mounts."

Analyses of the output tracings from the two widely separated instruments provide only probabilities, not certainties. Each coincidence must be a decisively strong response registered by each of the two detectors within the same brief period—less than half a second.

Every possible kind of check was made to eliminate the possibility that both detectors could be responding to one influence that was not of the nature of gravitational radiation. These tests appear to have eliminated the possibility of such alternative causes as cosmic rays and electromagnetic radiation of some kind. Seismic (earth) movements were ruled out by the sheer distance from Maryland to Chicago. Any quake or tidal shift would have required much more than one half-second between the time it "hit" each of the two detectors.

Statistical studies indicated that chance alone could account for, at most, a few coincidences per month. Yet during an 11 month period ending November 30, 1969, Weber found more than 100 such marked coincidences. He concluded that they could not all be the result of random or accidental causes.

During one period of less than three months, he operated several detectors in Maryland plus the one in Chicago, and recorded more than 17 two-detector coincidences, 5 three-detector coincidences, and 3 four-detector coincidences. And none, he found, could be traced to either electromagnetic or seismic events.

Various sophisticated methods were used to separate random from nonrandom observations. Thus Weber delayed by 2 seconds the signals from one of the two distant detectors, and counted the coincidences that now appeared. The number of coincidences dropped significantly and just about to the level that chance alone would call for.

Early in 1969 at a meeting of the American Physical Society, Weber reviewed additional data. For the first time he was able to link the detector responses with cosmic directions. Each of his detectors was placed so the axis of the cylinder pointed east and west. Arriving gravitational waves from outside the Earth should, according to theory, cause the ends of each cylinder alternately to move closer together and farther apart by very tiny displacements when the frequencies of the arriving waves matched the basic natural frequencies or resonance "modes" of the detector cylinders.

Now if an imaginary line were drawn from the Maryland detector to the Chicago detector and extended indefinitely in both directions, each of the two ends of that line would sweep through a full circle, or 360 degrees, as the Earth turns. At a certain time each sidereal (astronomical) day, one end or another of this line would point "upward" toward the center of our Galaxy; then, just half a day later, one end or the other of this line would point downward (through the Earth), in that same direction of the center of the Galaxy.

Weber's new analysis showed that about *two-thirds* of all his recorded coincidences were recorded in one or the other of those two positions. Somehow most of these seemingly simultaneous reactions were associated with influences emanating from the galactic center. It is there that cosmologists and astrophysicists would expect most of the violent events which would radiate gravitationally sizeable amounts of power.

Reports of such directional concentrations of the coincidences intensified the interest previously evoked by these difficult experiments. Ironically, and typically for our times, as the findings from these tests seemed to reach new levels of significance, the funding to maintain them was also reaching its end. In a period when grants for pure, rather than warfare-oriented, science were being cut drastically, the great problem of gravitational radiation was but one of many important projects to suffer.

One industrial organization, the Hughes Aircraft Company, has shown imagination by supporting gravitational radiation research to the extent of some $50,000 a year since 1965. At present, an astronaut from the National Aeronautics and Space Administration is working with Hughes on a wide-band detection antenna for such radiation. This antenna is to consist of masses placed in orbit at distances from 1 to 1000 km apart, linked only by a beam of laser light to report the relative motions of those masses.

Other plans for devices to detect and measure gravitational waves are under discussion elsewhere. A group at Stanford University seeks to use cryogenic (ultra-low-temperature) techniques to increase sensitivity and reduce the internal "noise level" of their detectors.

In the Soviet Union, whose theoretical physicists include several deeply involved in gravitational radiation as well as other theoretical aspects of general relativity, interest also appears to be quickening.

Difficulties of detection—Even with equipment far more sensitive and sophisticated than the pioneer devices used by Weber, the effort to detect and measure gravitational waves will not be easy. Constant thermal fluctuations of the atoms composing the aluminum cylinders result in incessant ultratiny average displacements of the cylinder ends, estimated at about 10^{-16} m (one ten-trillionth of a single mm). That is far less than the diameter of an atomic nucleus. Such thermal shifts form a background of "noise" and involve distortions of the cylinder's shape estimated at a few parts in 10^{-16}.

Against such a "noise" background, the detection system seeks to establish the additional strains that originated from the outside and the distortions that can be attributed definitely to gravitational waves. The detector cylinders used by Weber were "tuned", by their size and shape, to frequencies of about 1660 cycles per second. These frequencies were selected because they fit the financial possibilities. Also, there was reason to suspect that gravitational waves emitted during such an event as a super-nova explosion would "sweep through" this frequency with radiation of some power.

At the time of this writing a total of half a dozen detectors have been built and operated by Weber and his co-workers.

Their "antennas" have all been aluminum cylinders about 1.5 meters from end to end, and from two-thirds of a meter to one meter in diameter.

There appears at this time to be good evidence that gravitational radiation actually was the source of many, if not all, of the coincidences found between the widely separated detectors. However, the evidence is, as yet, far less certain than can be satisfying in science. To reach more solid evidence, it will be necessary to develop detectors in which the signal level equals or exceeds the average noise level. This has not been the case with pioneer detectors.

Computations by Weber suggest that, assuming the coincidences were caused by gravitational waves of frequency at or near 1660 cycles per second, the energy of such waves in each cubic kilometer of space around Earth must approach 10^{-3} joule. If that much energy is associated with a narrow bandwidth of frequency, then the total energy density of gravitational radiation of *all frequencies* must be enormous.

Using Weber's results, a group of "relativists" at Cambridge University—Dennis W. Sciama, G. B. Field, and M. J. Rees—have published estimates that total gravitational radiation from the center of our Galaxy may be as high as between 3 and 4 times 10^{49} joule per year. This is a staggering total, for it is equivalent to complete conversion into gravitational radiation energy of about 200 stars the size of our Sun, each year! The estimate is applied to our Galaxy because it must be assumed that the detectors thus far used would be incapable of responding to such radiation emanating from other galaxies far off in space.

If mass is actually being lost from the innermost region of our Galaxy at any such rate, the effects would inevitably be far-reaching. It would mean that the total gravitating mass in the galactic center would steadily decrease, that its gravitational field would weaken, and that stars previously in outermost bound orbits around the galactic center would reach escape velocity and leave the Galaxy, never to return.

Sciama and his group have, in fact, suggested that, in consequence of such considerable mass loss, our galaxy has been expanding, and that the expansion has gone on during at least the past 100 million years. They suggest that total mass lost within ten times that period—one billion years—would equal the present total mass in the Galaxy. This follows, since if the masses of 200 Suns are lost annually, in 10^9 years the loss would be 2×10^{11} solar masses, just about the present estimated mass of the entire Galaxy.

Observations have indicated that all the stars and gaseous matter in the general neighborhood of our Sun are moving away from the galactic center at about the same average velocities. Such a concerted "fleeing" from the galactic center conforms to the concept that the gravitational field of the Galaxy is weakening.

What would be the most obvious characteristic of a galaxy that had a "half-life" of one billion years—meaning that every billion years the galaxy's remaining mass would be reduced by half? Sciama has lately suggested that such a galaxy would retain no stars whose bound orbits around the galactic center had periods greater than one billion years. The observational evidence appears, thus far, either to support this suppostion for our Galaxy, or at least not to contradict it.

These and other hypotheses are stimulated by the first results of the efforts to detect and estimate the power of gravitational radiation reaching Earth from space. Like a ferment, the new gravitational concepts, including that of gravitational waves, encourage speculations and investigations in astronomy, astrophysics, and cosmology. This is a new situation in what had been, during centuries, a seemingly settled and tamed area of science. Not so much Newton himself, as some of his followers, would be surprised or even shocked. To them it seemed as if "the laws of gravitation" sufficed to answer all pressing questions about the universe. The unanswered questions were in other areas.

The situation was somewhat like that described by Arthur Koestler, a literary commentator on science, in his book *The Sleepwalkers*. Once, leading Greek observers had looked on stellar motions as a "wild dance." But after the Newtonian synthesis this area "was settling into a decorous and stately Victorian waltz." In such a well-regulated universe, deity was "reduced to the part of a constitutional monarch, who is kept in existence for reasons of decorum, but without necessity . . ." If concepts of gravitation lapsed into a state of "decorum" during a century or more, the past decade or two have unsettled them—and some strange, even startling, developments assuredly lie ahead, unless man's future is blighted by war.

Some possibilities—An obvious need exists to develop dependable devices for "broad band" detection of gravitational waves. This involves the use of detectors, or sets of them, able to respond to many frequencies, either at once or in swift and selective succession. We get this kind of reception today from a good radio set. Without changing the antenna or circuitry of the radio we can tune it to select any frequency from about 50 to 160 kilohertz in the medium wave band (1 kilohertz $= 10^3$ cycles per second).

As presently conceived, wide-band gravitational radiation antennas will consist of widely spaced masses between which a beam of light from a stable laser is reflected to detect the gravitationally-induced vibrations. The whole would have to be enclosed in a vacuum tank or long pipe, in order to keep out noise.

By means of electronic circuitry, the vibrations thus detected could be scanned selectively, and desired frequencies could be singled out in swift succession up and down the frequency scale, in order to show at which frequencies response is noted. This system is akin to what technicians call a "swept center frequency."

The future gravitational radiation detectors may also embody, by means not now apparent, sophisticated systems known as "chirp filters." This would be an instance of fashioning the trap to fit the habits of the intended prey, the prey being binary star systems, whose final death results in a "chirp" of gravitational radiation.

The binary star systems, believed now to make up an important part of the quarry of gravitational radiation seekers, are assumed —as we have shown—to radiate powerfully only in their final stages. It is then, in that swiftly accelerating final spasm of activity, that they spin ever more closely and rapidly until they finally come together. A narrow band receiver can catch but a slender sliver of that final rise up the frequency scale.

A rapid increase in both frequency and intensity produces the sound effect that we call a "chirp." The final phase of a collapsing binary should "chirp" also, in terms of gravitational radiations.

As this book is being written, two Soviet scientists, Vladimir Braginski and Eugene Popov, have completed preparations to repeat Weber's experiment, using nine cylinders as antennas, each sensitive to waves of about 1600 Hz (cycles per second). Their plan, as revealed at a conference on relativity held in New York, is to begin with two antennas, separated by perhaps 40 km. If significant coincidences are found, the next phase will be the use of a gravitational "telescope" or of another arrangement similar to a xylophone.

The telescope would be a pattern or array of nine gravitational detectors. Working together they could give greater sensitivity and some indication of the angle from which the waves appear to come. The detectors would be the gravitational equivalent of the radio telescope arrays that have done so much to supply information to radio astronomers in recent years.

The xylophone arrangement, on the other hand, calls for separate antennas, each tuned to respond to a different frequency, such as 800 Hz, 1000 Hz, 1200 Hz, 1600 Hz, and so on. If waves are arriving from binary neutron stars spiraling in toward each other, then the signals, increasing in frequency in the "chirp" effect, could be expected to be picked up by one antenna after another. Calculations made by an eminent theorist, Freeman Dyson, suggest that the time interval between responses at the various frequencies going up the scale should be about 0.2 or 0.3 seconds.

A detector designed especially to respond to low frequencies, in the range of 10 to 300 Hz, is being built by David Douglass at the University of Rochester, New York. Its massive antenna is in the shape of a square with the central portion cut out. It is hoped that this detector may, at about 60.4 Hz, be able to pick up gravitational waves from the famous pulsar in the Crab nebula. The spin period of that pulsar, as proved both by its radio "beeps" and its optical "blinks," is about 30.2 Hz. This is doubled, because of the special twice-frequency pattern shown in gravitational radiations, as already mentioned.

Experts agree that detectors already operated and under construction will some day seem as primitive as does the early laboratory equipment with which Heinrich Hertz once established the reality of electromagnetic radiations in the frequency regions we now call "radio."

Indeed, Vladimir Braginski compared these first gravitational wave detectors to crystal radio receivers from about the era of 1920. The next phase, he suggested, should consist of the equivalent of the "heterodyne" receivers that so greatly advanced radio communications. He and his associates have proposed plans for a quadrupole rotating receiver, with two dumbell-shaped masses revolving 90 degrees out of phase with each other. If they were rotated at a rate about one thousandth of a revolution per second different from the frequency of an incoming gravitational wave, then their alternate acceleration and deceleration of rotation should produce an effect like that of the "beats" of a heterodyne radio receiver. Enormous technical problems of reducing friction and maintaining vacuum for the revolving dumbells await solution now.

A most particular particle—Modern science has learned to look on light in two related but distinguishable ways: as electromagnetic waves, and as tiny particles of energy called "photons." Theory requires that gravitational radiations, too, have their own corresponding or equivalent particles. They have already been given an appropriate name—"gravitons." Characteristics of light photons are well known. Those of gravitation have been deduced, though no graviton, as such, has ever been isolated or "detected."

The graviton—like the photon, the electron, and the proton— must be a stable, long-lived particle. Like the photon, again, the graviton must be a particle without mass. This being the case, the graviton must always travel at c, the same velocity as that of light or radio in empty space. The graviton, then, cannot be slowed, halted, or trapped in a restricted space for examination. Again like the photon, the graviton can have no electric charge. It must be electrically neutral.

Like the photon, the electron, and many other particles, the graviton must have an additional characteristic called "spin." But the amount of magnitude of its spin is unique. Where the electron and the neutrino each have spin of ½, and the photon has a spin of 1 or unity, the graviton has—must have—a spin of 2.

"Spin" in modern particle physics is a subtle, somewhat esoteric concept. It should not be thought of as a literal rotation, but rather as intrinsic or built-in "angular momentum." It is a momentum which the particle possesses *in addition to* the angular momentum arising from the motion of the particle's own center. This spin has a peculiar property. We may choose any direction we wish in space. Then if we measure the spin, we shall find it is oriented either along, or opposite to, that direction.

Imagine a skater following a circular "orbit" around a marker on the ice, meanwhile twirling constantly as he goes. He has two kinds of angular momentum: the orbital and the spin. The sum of these remains constant, or is "conserved." And so it is with elementary particles. The graviton—assuming it indeed exists—has twice the spin momentum to conserve of any other known particle.

The family status of the graviton is also well-known in theory. It shares with the photon the distinction of belonging neither to the *baryon,* or heavy-particle clan; nor the *meson,* the medium-mass group; nor the *lepton,* the light-mass group. The graviton is, in fact, massless.

In some respects a haunting similarity has seemed to link the supposed graviton with an extraordinary observed particle known as the *neutrino.* The neutrino too is massless, or very nearly so. It too moves at the speed of light. During the early 1930s the great Danish atomic scientist, Neils Bohr, called for a study to determine whether neutrinos were, in fact, different from the particles underlying gravitation. In one respect, it seems, they are truly different: the neutrino has a spin of $\frac{1}{2}$, not of 2. The neutrino spin points backward, opposite to the particle's direction of motion.

A versatile physicist, the late George Gamow, in an interesting small book on gravitation, called attention to the fact that in the so-called "weak interactions," neutrinos are never emitted alone, but always together with other particles. Thus, the decay of a neutron gives rise to a proton, an electron, and a neutrino.

But, asked Gamow, may there not be processes in which only neutrinos and their opposite numbers, anti-neutrinos, are emitted? For example, an excited nucleus might give off, at once, a pair: a neutrino, and an anti-neutrino. The spin of the latter would point forward, in the direction of that particle's line of motion.

Such a pair, Gamow asserted, would have a combined spin not of $\frac{1}{2}$ plus $\frac{1}{2}$ equals 1, but of 2, like the spin of the theoretical graviton. Though he called it only "sheerest speculation," Gamow regarded the notion of a possible identity between neutrino and graviton as an "exciting theoretical possibility."

This is but one among the wide-ranging assortment of bold insights, hypotheses, or outright guesses that the new views of gravitation have stimulated.

10

The Significant Size of Big G, and the Possibility That It Changes

Every important gravitational "recipe," or equation, is based in part on G, the Newtonian gravitational constant. This is true for the equations that measure the static, or "near," gravitational effects; likewise it is true for the radiative or "far" effects of gravitational waves. In fact, though Einstein's general relativity equations are beyond the level of this book, they too make use of G.

Every complete table of the basic constants of physical science includes G. Yet there are far-reaching questions concerning G. Is it truly a *constant?* Is it the same everywhere in our observable universe, or are there perhaps great chunks of space in which its value would be greater, and some areas in which it would be less than in the region of our own Galaxy?

Has G always had the same value as it has now? Will it, in the future of our universe, remain always at its present value? Why does it have just the value that we find here and now: 6.67×10^{-11} m^3 kg^{-1} s^{-2}? Is there some fundamental connection between this numerical value and other magnitudes characteristic of the universe?

These are dizzying cosmic questions. Here we can only hint at some of the suggested answers. Our hints may help to illustrate how diverse and exhilarating are the investigations stimulated by the new approaches to gravitation. Such investigations link the vastest and most distant concepts with the tiniest and most immediate measurements that man can make.

Suppose, as a start, that this were a universe in which the numerical value of G were not 6.67×10^{-11} but 6.67×10^{-8}, or a thousand times greater. Obviously, gravitational effects would be a thousand times as strong as they are now, and it would be a very different universe, to say the least.

An important trend of thought in theoretical science holds that suppositions such as these are basically misleading. It is unrealistic, this viewpoint would say, to speculate whether any different value of G could be found in this universe, because the physical characteristics of this universe are just what determine the size of G. The size of this constant is quite simply a result of how matter is distributed throughout our universe; therefore no other magnitude of G is conceivable under these circumstances.

Such far-reaching conclusions—easier to state than to demonstrate or prove positively—are associated with a proposal tentatively advanced by the Austrian physicist, Ernst Mach (1838–1916), the same man whose name is identified with the number indicating the relation between the velocity of an aircraft and the velocity of sound in the same atmosphere.

Mach proposed that the inertia of every bit of matter resulted from the mutual interaction of *all* the matter in the universe. In other words, a mass resists acceleration because of the influence on it of all the rest of the masses everywhere. Einstein gave this far-reaching idea the name of "Mach's Principle," and decided that here Mach was on the right road. Relativity, in fact, conforms to Mach's Principle.

According to Einstein, several effects should be observed if this principle is to hold good. (1) The inertia of a body should show increase when the masses around it are increased. (2) If a hollow body is rotated, it should create inside itself a field, or influence, which deflects any body moving in that space—deflects it toward the direction of that rotation. (3) When masses around a test body are accelerated, that body should undergo an accelerating force, in the same direction as the acceleration of the surrounding bodies.

But motion is relative. In case (3) above, we could accelerate the test body with respect to all other bodies around it, and look for a corresponding force on the test body—a force that would now operate in the direction *opposed* to the direction of the acceleration. That force is, in fact, the *inertia* of the test body. It does operate to resist acceleration, and its strength is proportioned to the amount of matter (mass) in that test body.

In case (2), we could rotate our test body, which would be equivalent to spinning around it in the opposite direction all other bodies in the universe. The influence observable on the test body should now be a deflection in the direction opposite to that of its own rotation, but toward the direction of the *seeming* rotation of the "fixed stars."

Also, in this case (2) the test body should show a radial centrifugal field. The deflection actually observed on rotating bodies is called "the Coriolis effect;" and it is indeed accompanied by the radial centrifugal "field," often called centrifugal forces.

According to Mach's Principle and relativity, then, observations on a test mass should show the same results whether (a) the rest of the universe is accelerated relative to it; or (b) it is accelerated relative to the (average of) the rest of the universe. Also, whether (a) the rest of the universe is rotated around it; or (b) it is rotated relative to the (average of) the rest of the universe.

The phrase "fixed stars" is a common one to designate that average of the masses making up the rest of the universe. The phrase has more than poetic significance here, for it suggests the fundamental fact that in dealing with the effects of relative *accelerations* of masses, we deal with effects that diminish only as the inverse first power of distance (as $1/D$) and *not* as the inverse square of distance ($1/D^2$).

In short, the inertia-creating interaction is, like gravitational radiation, a "far" effect, not a "near" effect. The result is dramatically illustrated by an estimate made by D. W. Sciama of Cambridge University, a leading exponent of the validity of Mach's Principle. Using measurements of the amount of light received on Earth from a clear night sky, Sciama computed that only some 20 percent of the influences responsible for the inertia of bodies on Earth can come from stars and galaxies within the observational range of the giant 200-inch optical telescope on Mount Palomar, California. About 80 percent of that influence is thus traceable to the invisible army of heavenly bodies lying more than about 3×10^{25} m, or 2 billion light-years, distant from Earth.

Inertia is, in this view, the result of truly "far out" masses. What we call *gravitation*, and measure in units of force or acceleration, is a "near" effect, that falls off in proportion to $1/D^2$. What we call *inertia*, on the other hand, and measure in units of mass (the kilogram), is essentially a "far" effect, for it falls off, or diminishes, only in proportion to $1/D$.

Despite this basic difference, the total interaction of the myriads of masses composing our universe is such as to create a constant proportionality between M_i, the inertial mass of any body, and M_g, the body's gravitational mass. That striking identity was mentioned earlier in this book. Now, in terms of Mach's Principle, it appears as a result of the dual relationship— the acceleration-resisting part which we perceive as the inertia of any mass; and the attraction-producing part which we perceive as the gravitational strength of that mass.

What makes up our universe?—In his *Autobiography,* the late mathematician and philosopher Bertrand Russell told how in his youth when he expressed interest in philosophy his elders tried to discourage him by repeating a phrase: "What is mind? No matter! What is matter? Never mind!"

We cannot dismiss so glibly the question of how much matter there appears to be in our universe. It is assuredly an unlimited universe. There is no fence or boundary that marks where it stops—no "city limits" or "universe limits," beyond which one proceeds at his own risk. Yet it appears *not* to be an infinite universe. This can be made clear if we include in "our" universe only the objects that can conceivably be observed or responded to, and exclude all else as nonexistent for us.

Some years ago a great astronomer, Edwin P. Hubble (1889–1953), made a historic discovery. He found that the more distant galaxies seemed to be, the more their light, as received on Earth, was shifted toward lower frequencies—that is, toward the red. This is the famous "Doppler redshift," quite different from the "gravitational redshift" previously discussed.

This effect is always compared with the change in pitch of a train whistle: as it moves toward us we hear it higher than it sounds to the engineer on the train; as it moves away from us, we hear it lower. The more distant the source, the lower the "pitch" of its light to an Earth observer.

The poet Robinson Jeffers wrote:

> The learned astronomer
> Analyzing the light of the most remote star-swirls
> Has found them—or a trick of light deludes his prism—
> All at incredible speeds fleeing outward from ours.
>
> —*Margrave,* 1932

The "trick of light" refers to one hypothesis that was soon rejected by astronomers—namely, that in travelling long distances light itself somehow grew "tired" and lost energy, shifting toward the red frequencies. The dominant belief today is that Hubble identified an actual "fleeing outward," with velocity of recession proportional to the distance to the observed object.

Obviously, the Earth is not the stationary *center* in this cosmic process. From any other observation point, even from a planet in a most distant galaxy, the universe would present the same effect of "fleeing outward." Again a common analogy helps to clarify the situation. If we have a polka-dotted balloon and blow it up, as the ballon expands the distance along its surface between any two dots will increase. The rate, or velocity, of that increase will be proportional in every case to the measured distance between those two dots.

Hubble, basing his ideas on the best data available in the late 1920s, estimated the proportion between V, the velocity of recession indicated by extent of the red-shift of light, and D, the estimated distance of the light-emitting bodies. His ratio, which became known as H, or Hubble's Constant, was about 550 km per second per megaparsec. The latter is an enormous astronomical unit of length. When the ratio is worked out, we find that $H = V/D = 1/5.6 \times 10^{16}$s. In other words, Hubble's Constant, H, is actually a fraction whose denominator is a very large number of seconds, a long time.

What could correspond to that time period? It could be the period elapsed since all the "fleeing" galaxies were together in one great central clump that included all matter now scattered throughout the universe. Other interpretations are also possible. Whatever hypotheses may be offered, H remains a vital figure for the understanding of the apparent structure of the universe around us.

During more than 40 years since Hubble's first estimates, H has been revised. More and better data have caused the constant to be changed to a ratio close to 40 (rather than 550) km per second per megaparsec. That corresponds to an H of about 7.7×10^{17}s, or about 24×10^9 years.

Implied in the Hubble Constant, H, is also a most important distance limit, called the Hubble radius or "cosmic horizon." If each megaparsec of distance from Earth shows a velocity increase of 40 km s^{-1}, then galaxies at a distance of 7,500 megaparsecs from us should apparently be fleeing at a velocity of 300,000 km s^{-1}. But that is the velocity of light itself, c! Relativity long ago revealed that this was the absolute limit of observable velocity, anywhere in the universe.

Whatever galaxies are observable, whether by light, radio, or even gravitational radiations, must lie within that cosmic horizon of 7,500 megaparsecs—about 2.3×10^{26} m distant from us on

Earth. In fact, the redshifting or Doppler effect causes all radiations from objects at the cosmic horizon to suffer such energy loss that those objects simply fade out.

No use asking what lies "beyond" the horizon of our universe. Such questions are fundamentally meaningless, because unanswerable in principle as well as practice.

Why the sky is dark at night—The universal recession, measured by H, accounts for the fact that life is possible on Earth. If ours were an infinite and nonexpanding universe, then in whatever direction one looked there would lie, nearer or more distant, the surface of some star. The sky would be one great blaze of light, as though studded by a continuous mass of Suns. Temperatures on Earth would be thousands of degrees high. There could be no oceans, rivers, plants, animals, or men.

This was recognized almost a hundred years before Hubble by a German astronomer, Heinrich Olber (1758–1840). He called attention to the paradox, but could not supply what we would call a valid answer as to why this insufferable blaze of light did not exist. Only the process of expansion reduces the radiation we receive to a level that permits the chemical compounds of life itself to form and function.

Since our cosmic horizon seems to be about 2.3×10^{26} meters distant in all directions, what volume of space is thus within our "ken?" It is risky to assume that the geometry we use on Earth applies unchanged to these extreme limits of the observable universe. Yet it is a risk worth taking here. Our cosmic horizon or radius is converted into our cosmic volume in accordance with the "recipe" for the volume of a sphere with radius R: $V = 4/3\pi \ R^3$. And this represents a volume for our "available" space of about 6.8×10^{79} m^3.

Within that volume must lie all the mass and the energy—the matter and the radiations—which can interact on us and the objects around us on Earth. What is the amount of the mass-energy it contains?

Clues from the recipe for G — On the way to answering that, let us look again at the elements that make up G, the gravitational constant: $G = 6.67 \times 10^{-11}$ m³ kg⁻¹ s⁻². These units — measurements of meters cubed divided by kilograms divided by seconds squared — show that the "dimensions" of G are Length³/Mass × Time². This can be written in the form of the product of two fractions: $L^3/M \times 1/T$.

Now, L^3/M has a familiar look to physicists and engineers for it is the reciprocal, or inverse, of *density,* which always follows the pattern M/L^3. Also, $1/T^2$ is the square of a fraction whose denominator is a time or duration.

We have already found such a time period associated with the universe as a whole. It is the Hubble Constant, H, approximately $1/7.7 \times 10^{17}$ s. Also we have found a kind of universal volume, $L^3 = 6.8 \times 10^{79}$ m³.

We wish to test a guess — that $G = L^3/M \times 1/T^2$. We have figures already for G, for L^3, and for $1/T^2$, which we get by squaring H. We place the one unknown, M, at the left and the three knowns at the right, and find:

$$M = \frac{L^3}{T^2 G}$$

When we "plug in" the corresponding quantities, we find that $M = 1.7 \times 10^{54}$ kg. That is an enormous amount of mass plus mass-equivalent of radiation energy. If we relate it to the cosmic volume (L^3) we find that it represents an average density: $D = M/L^3 = 2.5 \times 10^{-26}$ kg m⁻³.

This may seem to be an extremely low average density — only 2.5 kg per 10^{26} cubic meters. However — and this is the climax of our cosmic computations — there seems to be good reason to believe that 2.5×10^{-26} kg m⁻³ is just about right for the average density of mass-plus-energy in the universe as a whole.

The visible matter in stars, galaxies, gas clouds, and so on, has much lower density than that. But to it must be added substantial amounts of intergalactic matter, including particles, burned out or collapsed stellar bodies, and so forth. The galaxies themselves occupy only about one-millionth of the volume of visible space. Even a very thin scattering of matter through space between the galaxies could increase by as much as 100 times the total mass in the universe.

The suggested "fit" of these figures — of the gravitational constant *G*, the Hubble constant H, and the estimated average density of mass in the cosmos — is essential to the view that the observed size of *G* results from the amount and distribution of matter. This is a view urged with particular intensity and interest by D. W. Sciama in two brief but stimulating books: *The Unity of the Universe* (1961), and *The Physical Foundations of General Relativity* (1969).

The relationship can be summed up compactly this way: $GDT^2 = 1$. Here D is average cosmic density of matter, and T is the same as 1/H, meaning the time period underlying the Hubble Constant.

Thus *G* is linked both to a time and to the density of mass in an apparently expanding universe. Does *G* itself perhaps change with the passage of time? Einstein's general relativity equation calls for an unchanging *G*, but other theories have supposed that *G* may be diminishing with time.

A shrinkage in *G* would be associated with a corresponding decrease in the average density of mass in space. Such weakening of gravitational strength would result in increases in the radii of the orbits of planets around the Sun, of binary stars around each other, and so on.

In fact, it has been estimated that if *G* were dwindling at a rate of about 3 percent in a billion (10^9) years, the Earth's circumference would expand by about 150 km in the same period. This could account for some of the shifting of continental masses and other evidences of movement in the Earth's outer layer (mantle).

Among theorists who have marshalled evidence tending to

support the concept of a diminishing G have been such scientists as P. A. M. Dirac of Cambridge and R. H. Dicke of Princeton.

These are but some of the abundant and bold speculations about the cosmic and long-term behavior of gravitation. A set of books the size of an encyclopedia would hardly suffice to do justice to them all. Here we can learn only some of the more useful ways to think about the "new" gravitation. One of these is to look on G as a proportion, valid at least at this time and in our part of space, that links together both gravitational and inertial forces. Both forces are proportional to the mass of any body on which they act, and that proportionality is "packaged" in the constant G.

We may also think of that magnitude of G as the inevitable outcome of the total quantity and the distribution of matter-plus-energy in space. The words "plus energy" are needed, for Einstein established firmly the principle that energy behaves like mass and vice versa, according to the equivalence $E = Mc^2$.

In the following final chapter we shall examine how gravitational energy, behaving in a masslike way, makes possible extraordinary interactions and enormous outpourings of energy in brief periods of time, by means of gravitational effects, and by means only of such effects.

11
Even Gravitation Gravitates

Einstein's general relativity theory calls for one more character-istic in gravitation that merits a final place here: Only gravita-tion, among all known physical interactions, behaves in a non-linear way.

Similarities have been shown between gravitational and electro-magnetic effects, including static, magnetic, and radiative situations. But these, like the strong (nuclear) and the weak interactions, behave *linearly*. Gravitation alone follows the non-linear "line."

Non-linear in this sense has nothing to do with straightness or curvature in the propagation of the various forces. When bodies interact *linearly,* then the total force on any test body is simply the *sum* of the separate forces that each body would exert if it alone acted on the test object.

The total *gravitational* force to which a test body responds cannot, however, be such a simple sum of forces, for the gravitational forces that all the bodies exert *on each other* alter their combined force on the test body. In fact, even a single dense body, by its own "self-gravitation", shows this typical non-linear behavior.

Newton's gravitational laws do not include non-linear effects. These are insights owed to Einstein and the relativists who have advanced his historic work.

Various phrases have been offered to summarize non-linearity.

It is said that gravitation itself gravitates; that every mass generates a gravitational field whose energy-content behaves like an additional gravitating mass. It has even been put into a jingle:

> Gravitons grow gravitons.
> It really should delight 'em:
> Non-linearly going on and on . . .
> Sans halt—*ad infinitum!*

Non-linearity is more than a novelty. It is essential for the energy bookkeeping that becomes increasingly important as massive stellar bodies shrink to smaller sizes and greater densities. We can show, step by step, that the concepts and equations supplied by Newton and his followers will not meet the needs of such energy-accounting in these extreme cases.

Here (Figure 11-1) is our Earth, its radius about 6.4×10^{11} m, its mass about 6×10^{24} kg, its average density about 5.52 times

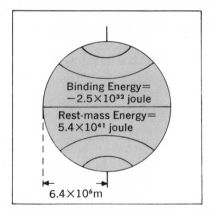

Figure 11-1. The binding energy of our Earth, a negative gravitational measure, may seem large, at -2.5×10^{32} joule. However, that number is reduced to insignificance alongside the rest-mass energy of the Earth, which is about 1½ billion (1.5×10^9) times as great—at 5.4×10^{41} joule. When the gravitational binding energy is insignificant alongside the rest-mass energy of a body, the "non-linear" behavior of gravitation plays little role.

that of water, or 5.52×10^3 kg/m³. If we assume that density if uniform throughout the Earth, the equation for its gravitational or "binding" energy is $E_b = 3/5 \times GM^2/R$. This is the total energy that would be needed to "unbind" the Earth, layer by layer, and remove its atoms to infinite distances against the pull of gravity. The fraction 3/5 appears because much more energy is required for such removal of 1 kg of mass from the outside (surface) layer of Earth than for the last or innermost kilogram, when the Earth has been peeled down like an onion.

The Earth, and also greater stellar bodies like the Sun, are not uniformly dense, however. They are far denser in their cores than near their surfaces. This variation tends to increase the gravitational energy for any given mass M packed into a radius R. Because of this and for greater simplicity, we shall here discard the 3/5 factor and use for our gravitational binding, or "scattering", energy E_b just this brief recipe or equation, for situations where Newtonian gravitational rules can be used:

$$E_b = - \frac{GM^2}{R}$$

And if we substitute the corresponding figures for our present Earth, we find a binding energy of -3.8×10^{32} joule. Again, the minus sign reminds us that this is the energy *needed* to scatter the entire mass of the Earth into a cloud of indefinite extent. It seems a great amount of energy. In fact, it represents an average of more than (minus) 6×10^7 joule for each of Earth's 6×10^{24} kilograms. We shall see, however, that this (negative) gravitational energy is tiny alongside the mass-energy which, from $E = Mc^2$, must be 9×10^{16} joule per kilogram. Earth's total mass energy is, in fact, about 1½ billion times its present gravitational energy.

The Sun, with about 330,000 times the mass of the Earth and about 109 times its radius, has about 3000 times Earth's average gravitational energy—or roughly 2×10^{11} joule per kilogram.

But mass-energy per kilogram is more than 20,000 times as great. In fact, the Sun's gravitational energy is about 45 parts per million of its mass-energy.

Shrinkage of massive bodies like the Sun, or even larger, can serve as a means of extracting energy, as we have seen. It can transfer or transform mass-energy into energy of heat, of radiation, and of motion (kinetic energy), while correspondingly increasing the (negative) gravitational energy.

The further such shrinkage continues, the greater become the gravitational forces seeking to pull the surface into still further shrinkage. Is there no limit? Could a body like our Sun, after it has shone through its thermonuclear burning phase, shrink ever smaller, and emit unlimited amounts of energy as it did so? If so, one great lump of matter could emit unending amounts of energy. It would be a case of something for nothing.

Let us illustrate, and then solve, this paradox, using examples of two massive bodies that attract each other. Here (Figure 11-2) we imagine a method of drawing power mechanically from two gravitating bodies, each a cold dwarf star, with mass of 2×10^{30} kg like our Sun, but compacted into a radius of 6.4×10^7 m like our Earth. They are placed here almost surface to surface, with just a weighing machine between. It registers a powerful force pulling them together—about 3.9×10^{35} newton, or about 8.8×10^{32} tons.

If we allow these masses to move closer by a distance of only 10 m, until their surfaces touch, then we could extract energy of up to 3.9×10^{36} joule from the operation. But we wish to increase that energy extraction. Hence we shrink these dwarfs still further until (Figure 11-3) each is only 1.6×10^6 m in radius. In addition to the heat emitted by each in that shrinkage, we find that when placed nearly surface to surface they attract each other 16 times as much as before, their centers being only 1/4 as far apart. If we let them move 10 m closer now, we could extract up to 3.9×10^{37} joule.

There is a feeling of power in these imaginary manipulations

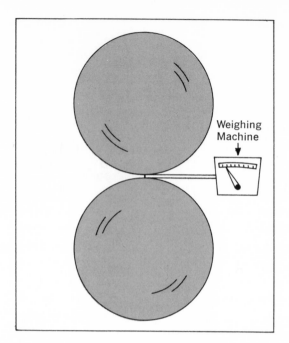

Figure 11-2. Two dwarf stars, with solar mass but Earthlike radii, placed with surfaces just 10 m apart, can generate energy, or do work, if they move to close that gap. One step in an impossible, but informative, "thought experiment."

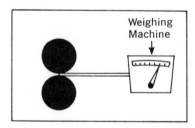

Figure 11-3. Shrunken to one-quarter their former radial dimension, these ultradwarf stars now are 64 times as dense as in Figure 11-2, and attract each other with 16 times the former force. If allowed to move closer together, they can emit 16 times more energy for each meter of such motion.

Shrinkage of large masses, accompanied by rising density, is the key to more rapid and complete extraction of energy from mass by gravitational interactions.

of great masses. So we shrink on, until each is down to a radius of only 6.4 meters, or one-millionth that of Earth. If we could now place their centers just 13.8 meters apart, then, by letting them move slowly 1 m closer, until their surfaces contacted, we should be able to extract up to 3.9×10^{47} joule additional energy.

But the combined masses of both ultra-dwarfs are 4×10^{30} kg, and their mass-energies, by $E = Mc^2$, amount to "only" 3.6×10^{47} joule. How can we talk of extracting *more* energy than there has been in the entire mass of the bodies involved?

Of course, it is an impossibility. We have used these imaginary manipulations to illustrate not what can be done, but what can't be done — and why.

Analogy of an energy bank — The way things work, in fact, may be compared to a great banking operation. This Bank of Universal Gravitation deals in energies, not currencies. Any body, or group of bodies, that we are studying can be regarded as an initial or opening deposit E_o in the bank. This is the so-called rest-mass of the body or bodies, at the $E = Mc^2$ rate of 9×10^{16} joule per kg of such mass, when it is scattered widely in space and quite at rest, as in some vast, motionless cloud of dust, before shrinkage sets in.

A rest-mass like that now in our Sun is thus an energy deposit of 18×10^{46} J. At first this is placed entirely in a kind of savings account E_a, representing the available energy still in the form of mass. We cannot make withdrawals directly from that account, for mass cannot be destroyed without trace. But we can make transfers of energy funds from this account E_a to a kinetic energy "checking account" E_k; and from it we can issue "radiation checks" — meaning we can emit radiations of heat, light, radio waves. Such radiated energies completely leave the body or bodies, and thus they diminish our combined energy balances in this bank.

Every process of radiation originates, in a very real sense, from kinetic or motion-energies that gravitational forces have imparted to particles of matter in these masses. Even the thermonuclear "burning" processes require violent motions by the atomic particles in the heart of the glowing stars.

After these operations have gone on for a time, we compare our various bank statements and check records, for they must balance exactly. The first rule is:

$$E_{rad} + E_{kin} + E_a = E_o$$

E_{rad} or total radiated energy means withdrawals or debits from the checking account. E_{kin}, being the thermal and kinetic energy in the remaining matter, means the balance still in that checking account. E_a or the mass still available as matter represents the balance still in the savings account. Together they must equal the mass energy with which we began the operation. But they must not exceed it, nor may they be less than it.

Now, if we add together the amounts E_{rad} and E_{kin} we find that they equal the energy which has been shifted from the E_a savings account into the E_{kin} checking account, from which it has either been radiated out, or left as a balance of kinetic and thermal energy in the bodies themselves. We can call this total of E_{rad} and E_{kin} by the name E_b, for it is identical in size with the binding, or gravitational, energy that the system under study has accumulated. All the debits or transfers from the E_a savings account constitute the E_b total. Since they are deductions or minuses, we can see the reason for insisting that a minus precede the numerical value for binding energy of any body or group of bodies.

Now we come to one more great, simple rule of this gravitational banking: $E_b + E_a = E_o$. Or we can put it this way: $E_o - E_b = E_a$. If the binding or gravitational energy E_b becomes as great as E_o, the rest-mass energy, then there is left no more available energy E_a. The savings account is exhausted. There is no way to continue the banking operation. The Universal Bank allows no energy overdrawals. It closes the account. The possibility of issuing additional radiation payments—light, radio waves, and the rest—disappears. So too does the star whose last stages we have illustrated by means of this banking analogy.

Even the "linear" view of gravitation supplied by Newton indicated that the E_b, or gravitational binding energy, would rise ever higher as a massive body shrank to smaller volumes and greater densities. But not until Einstein's earlier "special" relativity theory was it clear that the maximum available energy, the E_o, of matter was limited by the basic relation $E = Mc^2$. That sets the maximum amount from which withdrawals and transfers can be made in the Universal Bank's facilities.

Sooner or later, if the shrinkages can proceed to sizes small enough, there must come a time when the E_b equals the E_o and there is no more E_a or available energy to draw on. But how soon or how late does this point arrive? Newton's rules indicated that it came when shrinkage had gone a very great way. Then came Einstein's additional general relativity theory, with its non-linear content, and showed that it came sooner than the Newtonian theory called for.

The exhaustion of available energy is associated still with very small sizes, but at the same time with radii that are *double* what they would be in the non-linear Newtonian theory.

The factor 2 for non-linearity—The Newtonian approach would indicate that a body with mass like our Sun should reach the end of its available energies when its radius is 1.48×10^3 m or very nearly 1.5 km. The general relativity equations show, on the other hand, that this end point must come at 2.96×10^3 m, or very nearly 3 km—which is, of course, the "Schwarzschild radius" (R_s) already stressed.

In short, gravitational non-linearity causes E_b (the blocked-off binding energy) to grow more rapidly, for the gravitational forces themselves combine to act as if the remaining mass were greater by a factor that finally rises to the value of 2.

We can visualize this non-linear supplement as if it were a kind of ghost mass alongside the real one (Figure 11-4). As the shrinkage goes on, the mass seems to multiply itself, until finally in the familiar equations it is as if the old familiar factor G had become 2G. Thus the *relativistic* equation for the gravitational self-energy or binding energy of a single body of mass M and radius R becomes, in its simplest form: $E_b = 2GM^2/R$.

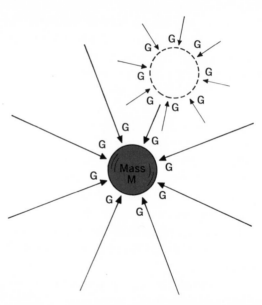

Figure 11-4. The non-linear "ghost" in the gravitational field is symbolized here. The solid sphere (shaded) is a mass M surrounded by its field lines, showing forces (and accelerations) directed toward its center. That is the *primary* gravitational field of M. But, symbolized by a broken line above, is the virtual or "as-if" mass—the secondary gravitational field which results from the mass-energy in the primary gravitational field.

The extent of that "as-if" mass is determined by the Einstein equation $E = Mc^2$, or rather by this form of it: $M = E/c^2$. This secondary gravitational field—plus the field of that field, and so on—is the basis for the unique "non-linear" behavior of gravitation. It underlies gravitation's unduplicated ability, when it becomes intense enough, to convert vast amounts of mass into energy in extremely short periods of time.

Similarly, the equation for gravitational potential ϕ when we deal with bodies at low gravitational intensities is $\phi = GM/R$. But bodies at very high gravitational intensities behave as if it were $\phi = 2GM/R$. And so on.

The swift shifting of energy from the available (E_a) to the binding energy (E_b) category is illustrated in a graph (Figure 11-5). As the size of the body shrinks (moving toward the right on the graph), the shaded area, indicating the E_b, rises until it becomes 100 percent. The solid or Newtonian line shows that, for a body with mass like the Sun, this limit is reached at about 1.5 km. The broken, or general relativity line, shows, however, that thanks to the non-linear behavior of gravitation, that critical radius lies at about 3 km.

In search of stability—Such a graph seems to suggest that all massive bodies sooner or later shrink all the way down to, and past, their ultimate Schwarzschild radii. We have earlier seen, however, that there are stellar fates which do not climax in collapse. This is true especially of stars less massive than the Sun. Some will find stability and permanence as dwarf stars, cold and dark, past the point of further shrinking. Others will shrink down to the state of neutron bodies, and survive there, having attained stability.

Elaborate calculations, based on plausible assumptions, have been made by a group of specialists in general relativity, including B. K. Harrison, Kip S. Thorne, Masami Wakano, and John A. Wheeler. They sought for stellar structures that could be considered stable, even after leaving behind their thermonuclear "burning" phase, and now being formed largely of iron, and cold iron at that.

Realistically recognizing that such bodies would have greater pressures and densities at their centers than elsewhere, they found it most meaningful to list the stable cases in the order of the densities developed in the central heart.

At a central density of about ten million times that of water

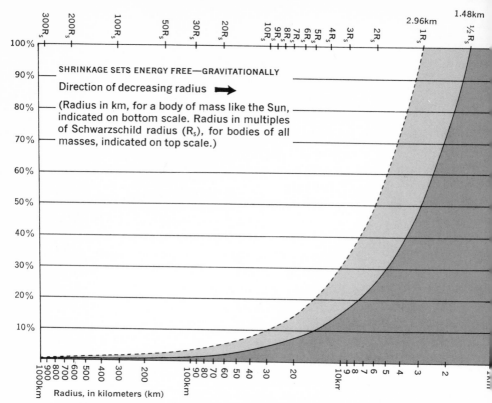

Figure 11-5. The shaded area, rapidly rising from less than 1 percent to 100 percent, shows the share of energy already emitted or transformed into thermal and motion energy, as a massive body shrinks. The shaded zone thus represents the binding energy, E_b, which diminishes and finally absorbs the last of the original mass energy, E_o, indicated by the white area.

The solid line shows how the process would take place according to Newtonian principles of gravitation, which are *linear* in approach. The broken line shows, in contrast, how they take place according to general relativity's non-linear principles. The ultimate point of no more available energy is reached at 2.96 km, rather than 1.48 km, because of gravitation's non-linear character.

We see that at $2 R_s$ (twice the Schwarzschild radius) available energy is still 50 percent of the total. At $3 R_s$ it is 67 percent (two-thirds) of the total. At $4 R_s$ it is 75 percent (three-quarters) of the total. And so on. Thus a vast part of the total mass energy remains available even after shrinkage has proceeded down to dimensions that seem very small by customary standards.

(10^{10} kg/m^3), they found stability for a body slightly less massive than the Sun, and with radius about 7.25×10^3 m. From that central density to one of about 10^{13} kg/m^3 they found stability should be possible for various masses greater than that of the Sun, up to about 1.4 times solar mass.

But beyond a central density of about 10^{13} kg/m^3 it seemed that only masses substantially below that of the Sun could be stable—could avoid collapse.

At 10^{17} kg/m^3 one finds a central density like that of nuclear matter. Here, the only indicated stable arrangements proved to have about one-fifth the mass of the Sun, and radii between 200 and 250 times their Schwarzschild radii. The calculations showed that such bodies would have about 1 percent of their energy "bound" (E_b) and 99 percent still available (E_a).

At still higher central densities of about 10^{18} kg/m^3 arrangements of such cold matter were found to show stability only with a mass about half that of the Sun, and a size about 8 to 9 times the corresponding Schwarzschild radius. Such a case showed 6 percent of its energy bound (E_b), 94 percent still available (E_a).

The highest proportion of bound energy (15.5 percent) was found in a stable arrangement with central density of 3×10^{19} kg/m^3 and a radius only 3.5 times its Schwarzschild radius. The mass here was also about half that of the Sun. These computations were carried all the way to supposed central densities of 10^{25} kg/m^3, suggesting nuclear matter *much compressed*. The stable cases found here all had masses notably less than that of the Sun, and showed bound energies of about 10 percent, leaving available the other 90 percent.

The implication of these studies is that collapse must ultimately overtake virtually all bodies with more than about 1½ solar masses, and a considerable part of all other bodies whose remaining masses range down to and even below that of the Sun. Also, it appears that these gravitational collapses will begin while the binding energies (E_b) of the body have climbed to no more than one-seventh or one-sixth of the original rest mass energy (E_o).

The remaining available energy (E_a), representing 85 percent or more of the maximum possible, must either be radiated away rapidly during the brief period of collapse itself—or be carried "down the black hole" as part of the vanishing body.

The swiftness of the slide to nothing—Though the collapse process seems to an outside observer to last indefinitely long, to the imaginary observer on the surface of the collapsing body it is a last ride completed in extraordinarily short time. The approximate duration T for a body of radius R and mass M is given by a peculiar equation:

$$T = 2 \left(\frac{R^3}{MG} \right)^{\frac{1}{2}}$$

What would be the apparent T for an observer on a body of Sun-like mass that had shrunken to just 100 times its R_s, or to 3×10^5 m, when its final collapse began? Only about 3×10^{-5} seconds! Even for a body far less dense—say one with average density no greater than that of water on earth, but with a total mass great enough to initiate gravitational collapse—the duration would seem no more than about 60 minutes.

What is the fate of the remaining energies, the E_a, that the body has when the collapse process begins, but which cannot be "unloaded" (radiated away) during the collapse itself? There seems no possible way to conceive an answer other than this— those energies are carried on down "the black hole." These energies are, in short, still operative as masses; they continue to gravitate, even though they belong to what is now a "body" of *zero* volume, a body that cannot be seen by means of light or listened to by radio receivers anywhere.

This is a realm of many bold conjectures and few certainties. The present weight of opinion seems to be approximately this: If, when collapse starts, a star is not spinning or is spinning only slowly, then during the collapse process it may radiate away up to about 9 percent of its remaining energy (its E_a). If, however, it begins its collapse when it is spinning at the fastest rate short of sheer physical disruption, such as about 1000 times a second, then it may convert into radiations up to about 40 percent of that remaining energy. This is a range of possibilities of about 1 to 4.

Either end of this range remains a most impressive outpouring of energy. The lower end represents from 4 to 8 times the energy radiated all during the previous nuclear burning period, when the body shone like a "normal" star. The upper end represents from 20 to 35 times that much energy.

Many painstaking studies are being made of possible mechanisms for such high-power emissions—incredible outpourings of energy in the collapse phase itself. Beside the possible gravitational radiations from a swift spinning star whose unsymmetries are intensified as it collapses, there are suppositions that vast floods of neutrinos, massless energy particles travelling at the speed of light, are poured out in all directions, before the gravitational field becomes so intense that nothing further can leave the vanished remnant of what was once a star.

Singular states around a singularity—What could be the aftermath of such an ultimate collapse? Where the shrunken star had been, there remains an extraordinary "state of affairs," commonly called a "singularity" by relativists. We cannot describe in helpful terms what has happened *to* the collapsed body, but we can suggest rather concretely what it will continue to do to other bodies that may come into its neighborhood.

How can we define that zone or region of space? Ordinary measures of meters and seconds become almost meaningless where space-time has been so stretched and distorted. However, we can indicate measurements in terms of the Schwarzschild radius of the mass that remained when the body went down that

A grin without a cat—and gravitation without a see-able star! This analogy has been made by Dr. John A. Wheeler, among other theoretical physicists. The collapsed stars, invisible but still gravitating, are like the disappearing Cheshire-Cat which caused Alice in Wonderland to reflect, "I've often seen a cat without a grin, but a grin without a cat! It's the most curious thing I ever saw in my life."

In its singular state, or "black hole," the collapsed star would have faded altogether or almost out of sight, but still the region roundabout would reveal its gravitational attraction—like the catless grin, most curious among the wonders of Wonderland.

This is one of the famous "Alice" drawings by John Tenniel.

black hole. Once again, let up suppose that we deal with such a mass equal to that now in our Sun: 2×10^{30} kg, for which the Schwarschild radius is very nearly 3 km.

Here (Figure 11-6) is an imaginary map of significant zones around such a "singularity," symbolized appropriately by a question mark at the center. The first zone, at (1), is that of the Schwarzschild radius itself. From this zone no light or other radiation can pass to the outside. Because of the slowing-down effect, outside observers might still seem to see very dimly a starlike body a little larger than this radius, as they received the dwindling and reddened waves emitted just before the actual plunge past this point occurred in the continuing collapse.

Next is the zone marked (2) at 1.5 Schwarzschild radii. It has two related features. Once any visitors from outer space, whether they be high-energy particles, cosmic rays, or satellites, come to this limit, they must be drawn down into the "black hole." They cannot escape the singularity. Also, if a star were

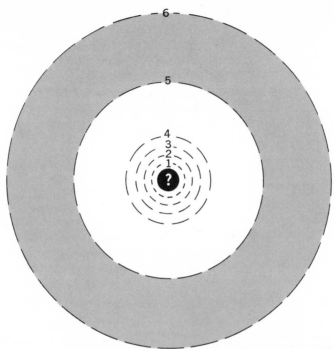

Figure 11-6. Critical radii or zones around a gravitationally collapsed body that has gone "down the black hole" suggested at the center. Each of these is based on insights afforded by general relativity, for Newton's rules for gravitation do not imply them.

The region near a "black hole" must be one of intense gravitational potential, and corresponding distortions of spacetime. Ordinary methods of measurement do not apply. If they did, and the "vanished" body took with it a mass twice that of the Sun, then the radius of inmost circle (1), the gravitational or Schwarzschild radius, would measure just 6 kilometers (6×10^3m), and the other radii would be in proportion.

The shaded zone between circles (5) and (6) suggests the sizes of neutron stars with corresponding mass. Collapse begins from within this zone and continues, accelerating without pause, until the shrunken body vanishes within the Schwarzschild radius (1).

shrunken to just this 1.5 circle and a beam of light were projected horizontally (that is, tangent to its surface), that beam would be so bent by the intense gravitation that it would follow the star's surface all the way around. It would, so to speak, endlessly orbit the star.

Next, at (3) lies the 2 R_s limit, within which no planet, asteroid, or space-vehicles could orbit the singularity. The reason is simple. To orbit here, their speed in orbit would have to be c, the velocity of light itself. Nature does not permit observers anywhere to see bodies or perceive energies moving in excess of c. Result: this circle is where the orbiting of bodies ends and the bodies are drawn down to the zero-volume collapsed mass.

At (4), about 2.6 R_s from the singularity "hole," is a capture zone for light, radio, or other radiation from the outside. If they once pass within this limit, they will be trapped and never emerge again from that sphere.

Finally, between (5) at about 5.8 R_s, and (6) at about 10 R_s, is suggested a zone. It is within this approximate size range that "neutron stars," if they had masses like the Sun's or greater, may have paused just before undergoing total collapse and forming the singularity at the center.

Goodby forever? — Are collapsed stars, vanished into their singularity sites, lost forever? Are these fantastic "black holes" tunnels of no return? A few theorists have boldly speculated that collapsed bodies could reemerge from the singular state — not where they had been, but somewhere else in the universe: at a different place and time. In this view, the "black holes" are like wormholes that have exits as well as entrances.

A reemergence would be an explosion rather than an implosion. It would be like a running-backward of a film of the original collapse which carried the star outside our ken. The huge outpourings of power observed, through radio waves, from the quasars, are — in this view — possibly instances of such explosive reemergence of energy from black holes.

More than forty years ago, James Jeans, a well-known British astronomer-writer, suggested that the centers of what we now call the galaxies may serve as "singular points" from which "matter is poured into our universe from some other, and entirely extraneous, spatial dimension." Such sites, Jeans noted, would appear to be "points at which matter is continually being created."

The need for non-linear treatment is apparent in gravitational fields so intense as those found around collapsed and collapsing bodies of stellar masses. But it would be misleading to assume that non-linear equations do not also help to account for physical effects observed around our own Sun, which is so far from being near to collapse that its surface extends into space about half a million times beyond what would be its Schwarzschild radius R_s.

The case of the improper precession—Einstein and relativity were first called to the world's attention in 1919, just after the end of World War I. An expedition of British astronomers had observed an eclipse of the Sun and measured the apparent displacement of stars whose waves of light passed close to the Sun's disk on their way to Earth.

Newtonian theory called for light to be bent somewhat by the gravitational effect of a massive body like the Sun. In fact, there was an equation for calculating the angle A through which light should be deflected when passing within distance D of the center of a body with mass M like the Sun:

$$A = \frac{2GM}{c^2 D} \text{ radians}$$

(A radian is an angle equal to about 57.3 degrees.)

General relativity, which Einstein had unveiled just three years earlier, called for a different deflection. Its angle was just twice that given by the above equation. (Again the factor 2, based on the non-linear behavior of gravitation.)

The results of the eclipse measurements, announced in 1919, were far from satisfactory; but they did tend to support the double, or Einstein, angle rather than the Newtonian one. Eclipse observations then and since are difficult and dubious.

If it depended on them alone, the case for general relativity might be very weak, even today. There are, however, other effects observable and observed at distances far beyond the surface of the Sun itself: for instance, the motions of the planet Mercury, whose average distance out is about 19 million times the Sun's Schwarzschild radius.

Mercury's orbit is slightly elliptical. Hence, when it is closest to the Sun, at its "perihelion," it is moving through a region of slightly greater gravitational potential than at its "aphelion," when it is most distant from the Sun. According to the non-linear Newtonian equations, Mercury should retrace its 86 day orbit exactly, excepting to the extent which that orbit is influenced by gravitational attraction of the other planets, or by the lack of a completely spherical distribution of mass around the center of the Sun.

For centuries, however, it has been known that Mercury's motion was different from that which could be accounted for by these influences. The close-knit spirals it traces around the Sun (Figure 11-7) move forward, or "precess" to an extent that is greater by about 7/10 of 1 percent than can be accounted for by Newtonian principles. It is a most minute discrepancy—a mere 42.6 seconds of arc per century. Yet it created large problems for scientists.

When Einstein perfected his general relativity equations, he found that their non-linear content called for the orbits of planets to precess or spiral to an extent related to the differences in the gravitational fields they moved through at perihelion and aphelion. For Mercury, he found the perihelion advance should be just about 43 seconds of arc per century. And this nearly perfect fit between theory and observation was merely a by-product, not the purpose of his great work.

General relativity predicts smaller perihelion precessions for Venus, Earth, Mars, and others for which observational confirmations are far more difficult than for Mercury. However, during the late 1960s observations on the asteriod Icarus gave good

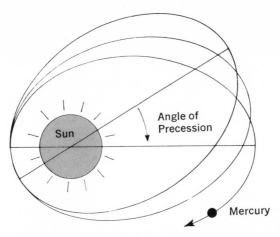

Figure 11-7. Mercury's orbital path embroiders endless spirals around the Sun, as suggested here in a simplified and exaggerated diagram. The perihelion, or line of greatest distance from sun to satellite, moves ahead with each orbit. Here is shown the angle of advance from one orbit to the second full orbit following. The actual precession is very small: about 260 orbits being required for an advance of just 1° of angle. Of this, less than 1 percent cannot be accounted for by Newton's rules of gravitation. That stubborn remainder requires Einstein's great general relativity extensions and corrections of Newton's work.

agreement with the perihelion precession predictions of general relativity.

In June, 1970, two separate teams of radio astronomers from the California Institute of Technology repeated with radio waves from quasars the historic observations of the eclipse of 1919. That is, they measured the extent to which the Sun's gravity deflected the waves (radio, not light) that passed close to the Sun's disk. The first results showed deflections of 1.77 and 1.88 seconds of arc. Einstein's theory called for 1.75 seconds, while a rival relativity theory, that of R. H. Dicke and C. H. Brans, calls for about 1.65 seconds. These angles are somewhat less than that made by the diameter of a dime at a distance of one mile. Later tests of the same kind will doubtless reduce the uncertainty of these pioneer radio measurements by as much as 60 to 80 percent.

Even as these lines are written, new and persuasive evidence is made public tending to support the original Einstein general relativity of 1916 rather than the Brans–Dicke modification. Dr. John D. Anderson, head of an experimental group at the Jet Propulsion Laboratory, Pasadena, California, announced late in 1970 that radio signals beamed from Earth to the spacecraft Mariner VI and back again, had returned with a lag or delay of about 204 microseconds (204×10^{-6} s). Mariner VI, at the time of this test, had reached a distance from Earth about two and one-half times Earth's average distance from the Sun.

The radio signals had passed close to the Sun, both on the way out *to* and the way back *from* Mariner VI. According to Newton's theory of gravitation, those signals should have traveled throughout at the usual space velocity of light, *c,* or 3×10^8 meters per second. That would have meant an elapsed time of some 43 minutes, or 2580 seconds. According to the Brans–Dicke theory, the Sun's gravitational field should cause an added delay of about 186 microseconds. But according to Einstein's general relativity theory that delay should be 200 microseconds at that distance.

The delay actually measured was 204 microseconds. This fell within expectable error limits of the Einstein prediction, but was unacceptably far from the Brans–Dicke prediction. For the time being, it seems that the most sophisticated experiments show that Einstein was right, here, as in so many other areas of science theory.

This extraordinary test, or series of hundreds of related tests, involved transmission of 200,000 watts of directed radio power from a huge dishlike steerable antenna at Goldstone, near Barstow, Nevada. The lag or delay noted in the returned signal was attributable solely to the retarding, or slowing down, effect of increased gravitational intensity in space around the Sun. That effect had never been suspected prior to Einstein's epochal general relativity theory.

In this historic series of tests, the maximum noted retardation amounted merely to about 4 parts in a billion (4 in 10^9)! The equipment used, however, is capable of measuring total elapsed time—transmission to reception—to within about 1/5 of 1 microsecond (or 2×10^{-7} s). That tiny time interval corresponds to a distance change of about 30 meters between the responding spacecraft and Earth.

Such extreme precision and sensitivity permits the present period—the 1970s and 1980s—to become the era in which, at last, general relativity in all its principal variations and versions, can receive the acid test of actual experiment and measurement. Beside the original Einstein and the Brans–Dicke varieties there have also been relativity modifications proposed by Peter G. Bergmann, an eminent physicist once associated with Einstein at Princeton, N. J.

Choices between such "rival" relativity theories, or between any of them and the Newtonian theory, could not conceivably be made under ordinary laboratory conditions on Earth. The differences would be far too tiny to detect. However, on the scale of the solar system; and, even more, on the scale of distant pulsars, quasars, and galaxies, such differences become not only detectable but indispensable to interpretation of observed effects. Moreover, the neutron stars, now so widely discussed and so generally assumed to exist, would not be possible, even as conjectures, under Newtonian gravitation theory. Only relativity provides the theoretical tools for comprehending them.

Final observations—The astronomical events of "incredible grandeur" include explosions more vast than the imagination can encompass. Entire galaxies, as big as our own or bigger, are rent by violences which, it has been said, "make a supernova explosion of a star appear as a firecracker compared with a big bomb."

Such is the heavenly object known sometimes as M82, sometimes as NGC 3034. (Figure 11-8). This is a negative made in

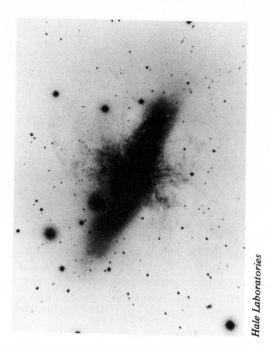

Hale Laboratories

Figure 11-8. Photographed as a negative to preserve the utmost detail of a typical event of "incredible grandeur," this is the vast exploding galaxy called M82. Its basic shape is, or was, spiral, like our own galaxy. From deep within the central core a super-super-explosion has projected matter in vast streamers and filaments, in both directions along the general line of the "axis of rotation." Material is ejected over distances of thousands of light-years, with tangles and turbulence that hint at the titanic forces at work. (The large black circles with dark "haloes" are individual stars, much nearer to us. They are not part of the catastrophic event happening to M82.)

blue light by the greatest of all present optical telescopes, that on Mount Palomar, California. Streams of ejected matter are seen, shot from the nucleus or center of the spiral galaxy over distances of 25,000 light-years in a "super-super-explosion."

Other recorded events involve ejections of material in blasts more closely channeled or directed (Figure 11-9). The object called sometimes M87, sometimes NGC 4486, is a large spherical galaxy, a sort of titanic star cluster of vast mass. A fantastic

Figure 11-9. A giant jet from the core of a great galaxy is one of the spectacles of "incredible grandeur" regarded as a result of processes of gravitational collapse and energy-release. This view, in polarized light, shows a vast spherical galaxy known as M87, out of which explodes in well defined direction a mass of luminous matter. That shaft, itself almost a miniature universe, is so vast that our entire solar system would not even appear as an identifiable dot alongside it.

jet of luminous matter emerges from it, rushing out over a distance of many thousands of light-years.

In almost all instances of such "incredible" upheavals, the core or heart of a galaxy appears to be the source for the swift outpourings of energy. So many instances have been found that it is believed some galaxies may even undergo more than one such catastrophic outburst within their galactic lifetime. Some evidence even suggests that our own particular Galaxy at least once underwent such a super-explosion from its very core.

Various suggestions were offered in the effort to find possible sources for the release of so much power, which thermonuclear processes obviously could not supply. Proposals included collisions between entire galaxies, chain-reactions of super-nova star explosions, or even encounters between masses of matter (our kind) and anti-matter (the "other" kind). But none of these suggestions seemed suited to fit the demands—for up to 10^{53} joule of energy had to be unleashed somehow to account for them.

As this book is written, gravitational collapse of super-stars or multiple collapses of large stars at galactic centers seem to be the only likely contenders for the title of "cause" of the incredible grandeurs.

In a final survey of collapse possibilities, we may repeat that a mass, if it is sufficiently great, may be ripe for collapse even though it does not have great average density. A body with mass 1000 times that of the Sun might show average density little greater than that of the Earth, yet be bound for collapse.

What about the greatest of all conceivable aggregations of matter—our universe itself? Could it be in line for a great gravitational collapse? In Chapter 10 a rough estimate was made of the observable size (radius) and average density of the universe. These estimates indicate a total mass content of about 1.3×10^{53} kg within our cosmic horizon, which lies some 2.6×10^{26} m distant in every direction. For a mass of 1.3×10^{53} kg, the Schwarzschild radius should be about 1.9×10^{26} m. Our estimated cosmic radius is only about 37 percent greater than this. And if our universe, within its cosmic radius, actually includes mass-energy equivalent to 1.8×10^{53} kg rather than 1.3×10^{53} kg, then our cosmic radius would be *at* the Schwarzschild radius!

If the observable universe is indeed already "at" its Schwarzschild radius, one can conceive more readily why it continues to contain "all there is," and why all radiation or energy emitted within it remains (so far as can be ascertained) within it—just as they must within any aggregate of matter shrunken to its Schwarzschild radius.

There are even more hypotheses in this direction. Is the universe itself undergoing, or about to undergo, the greatest of all gravitational collapses? Kip S. Thorne, a theoretical physicist specializing on such problems, has suggested that we may all be "trapped" within this universe, and that man "cannot avoid collapsing with the entire cosmos."

Since such a collapse could not come for some 7×10^{10} years, mankind has time first to deal with other, more pressing problems, such as how to avoid self-destruction through war.

Would a totally collapsed universe proceed, as if through a black wormhole, to reemerge later in some great burst or explosion? That comes quite close to the cosmological hypothesis sometimes called "the pulsating" or "the oscillating" universe depicted most imaginatively in "The Great Explosion," one of the last poems of Robinson Jeffers. He wrote in part:

> The universe expands and contracts like a great heart.
> It is expanding; the farthest nebulae
> Rush with the speed of light into empty space.
> It will contract, the immense armies of stars and galaxies,
>   dust-clouds and nebulae
> Are recalled home, they crush against each other in one
>   harbor, they stick in one lump
> And then explode it, nothing can hold them down; all that exists
> Roars into flame, the tortured fragments rush away from each
>   other into all the sky, new universes
> Jewel the black breast of night; and far off the outer nebulae
>   like charging spearmen again
> Invade emptiness.
>
> *— The Beginning and the End,* 1963

Hypotheses and speculations proliferate. Meantime, the solid foundations of observation and measurement are extended. Theorists find ever more material to work with. Not since Newton opened an era with his *Principia,* has there been such a ferment in thinking about gravitation and devising methods for ferreting out its secrets.

Coming decades will surely develop concepts not now known or dreamed of. It hardly seems likely, however, that they will depart from the concept that gravitation, alone among known physical interactions, operates in a non-linear manner, and thus can release unmatched amounts of energy from great aggregations of matter.

Future progress will no doubt bring clearer concepts of how such gravitational collapse can convert its released energies swiftly into floods of particles, magnetic and radio effects, and gravitational waves. However, even when such intermediate mechanisms are better defined and described, gravitational interaction will remain their ultimate root and source.

Alone among the interactions of nature, it seems, gravitation is able to unlock from matter energies sufficient to supply the events of "incredible grandeur" that we have here sought to introduce and illuminate.

Index

About the Author

H. ARTHUR KLEIN was born in Manhattan and lived briefly in Nebraska and Europe before his family settled in Southern California. He majored in English at Stanford University, and received a Master of Arts degree from Occidental College at Los Angeles.

Mr. Klein worked in London and Berlin as a reporter and feature writer for news services for several years, and then returned to the United States to work as a publicist, writer, and college teacher. He now devotes full time to writing and is an active member of the National Association of Science Writers. Mr. Klein's other books in the INTRODUCING MODERN SCIENCE series include *Masers and Lasers, Fuel Cells, Bioluminescence,* and *Holography.* He is also the author of *Surfing.*

The Kleins live on the beach at Malibu, California.

F

S: